Voices from Bangladesh

Voices from Bangladesh

Anupama Barua

To

Mr. Cartwright

Please enjoy
reading.

Leave a review in
Amazon.

Anupama
22.3.23

© Anupama Barua, 2021

Published by Dr Anupama Barua

A CIP catalogue record for this book is available from the British Library.

ISBN 978-1-7398901-0-0

Book layout and design by Clare Brayshaw

Cover flag © Oleg Kachura | Dreamstime.com
Crowd © Robert Adrian Hillman | Dreamstime.com

Prepared and printed by:

York Publishing Services Ltd
64 Hallfield Road
Layerthorpe
York YO31 7ZQ

Tel: 01904 431213

Website: www.yps-publishing.co.uk

Dedicated to my wise Father and helicopter Mother
This could not be completed without your blessings.

Contents

Preface

The country of my birth, Bangladesh, is a fairly new nation on the political map of the world, but the enriched culture and heritage of the Bengalis is centuries-old. These little stories are meant as a series of vignettes, offering a kaleidoscopic view of present-day life in Bangladesh in all its multifaceted complexity and the many entwined strands and layers of this emerging society.

I wonder what image my readers have of Bangladesh today. My French teacher, when heading off to work in Chittagong in the nineties, confessed to imagining a place of floods and mosquito swamps, home to half-naked skeletons begging with broken bowls. That media stereotype should have faded by now. There have been many changes recently and the picture today is more likely to feature garment factory workers or a low-paid migrant labourer sending money home from the Middle East. Other aspects of deep-rooted culture, the battle for life and the discrimination against sex, beauty and religion are rarely covered by the press and so are invisible to most outsiders.

But these are the topics I have tried to illustrate in my snapshots of Bangladeshi life. The characters in them are drawn from my own experiences and observations but are amalgamations, whose voices are distilled from the voices of many. Dr Ali, for example, in "All for One Stitch" is a composite of dominating males in a discriminating society, of a type that can be seen everywhere including the UK where I have made my home.

James Joyce wrote his famous book about Ireland while living in Paris, and it is said that it is much easier to write about the country of your birth when you live abroad. Certainly, my story about "The Library" in Bangladesh benefited from my shock and delight at finding such well-appointed and richly provided libraries in the UK – libraries that are now under threat. "You don't know what you've got till it's gone." And being able to travel perfectly freely with my dual passports, has given me a perspective on the "perfectly imperfect" difficulties encountered by immigrants worldwide and inspired "The Green Passport".

All these stories were written and compiled in a very short period from May 2021 to July 2021 but had been brewing for a long time; and my hope is that they will provide readers with an insight into the varied lives and life-struggles of the people of Bangladesh.

Anupama Barua
12th August 2021

Acknowledgements

Firstly, I would like to thank my father, the late Dr Sitangshu Bikash Barua, who allowed me dare to dream and who trusted and supported me in coming to the UK on my own. His sense of fairness and justice is evident in most of the stories. I have also to thank my mother, Mrs Romeli Barua, who encourages me with constant questioning and attention to the detail of life. I am deeply grateful for her willingness to be open about her experiences during the Bangladesh Liberation War.

My special thanks are due to Dr Giles Goodland, the lexicographer of Oxford dictionary and poet who, at the very beginning of my journey, encouraged me to write the first story and helped me to compose and structure them ready to present to readers.

I would like to say a special massive thank you to Mr Tom Wakefield, my piano teacher, for his painstaking revisions. I probably drove him mad by sending emails at two or three in the morning, but he supported me without complaint, and I am grateful for his patience and enthusiasm. His careful reading of the manuscript, his valuable comments and his devoted time and effort have helped me to correct many mistakes and find ways to give the stories a variety of different perspectives.

I also gratefully acknowledge the support of Mr Martin Riley as a writer and adviser. Although I did not heed his suggestion to edit the stories for the next nine months before publishing this book, I will follow his advice to "read, read and read" and "edit, edit and edit" for future writing projects. He was sent to me by a cosmic power to fulfil my dream to publish the book and has helped me in my last crucial steps to find a proofreader and a publisher.

Finally, I would like to express my gratitude to my husband Dr Biplab Barua and my daughter Arushi Barua Aurora for their patience and forbearance in the face of my continuing need to work at these stories alongside my day job.

The Conflict

Sumana was ten, with one younger brother and one younger sister. They lived in a big house that belonged to their grandparents, along with her grandmother, Uncles Mrinal, Badal and Sajal, and Aunt Lila. The house was divided into two parts, a brick section where there was a sitting room, three bedrooms, toilets and shower room, and the thatched section which held the kitchen, dining room and three more bedrooms.

Secretly, Sumana was happy that her school had been closed for the last couple of weeks. She was not a bright student; the maths homework was difficult and the teachers were not very kind or helpful. With the school closed, she spent most of her time in the playground. One day, while playing, she saw houses burning on the horizon but did not understand whose houses they were or who had set them on fire.

Sumana ran home from the playground and decided to play with Aunt Lila.

"Pishi," (the traditional address for a paternal aunt) "can we play Snakes and Ladders?"

Lila replied: "I am not in the mood to play."

Sumana continued nagging: "Why not, please Pishi, please. It is so hot; we cannot play Ha-du-du outside."

"Did you not see the fires? The Pakistani Army is torching the houses. I am concerned."

Sumana took out her drawing book and tried to draw houses in flames. Aunt Lila was hovering over the radio. It said that Pakistan unleashed genocide in Dhaka.

Her father came home from the office at five o'clock that evening, earlier than his usual time. He asked everyone to pack quickly: they had to leave the city. The Pakistani Army had reached Chittagong and it was not safe to stay there anymore. The family should grab their essentials and head for the village. Sumana put all her dresses and books in her school bag. She could not fit any toys in and did not have even space for her drawing book. Her grandmother crammed her Singer hand-crank sewing machine in the trunk. Aunt Lila and her mother were busily sewing gold jewellery into their petticoats so that no one could find it. Aunt Lila also sewed hidden pockets for cash. Her Uncle Mrinal had cerebral palsy and could not do much and was shouting to everyone. Uncle Badal was coming with them to the village, but Uncle Sajal was an intern at Chittagong Medical College Hospital and could not abandon his duties.

Her grandmother called Sumana's father to her for a serious discussion.

She said: "I cannot understand why we are going to the village, it would be better to go to India, like my sister and most of our neighbours. My sister has a big house. We'll be safe staying with her."

"Don't be silly, mother. I do not believe the tale of your sister. They are in a precarious condition in Calcutta. That city is on a knife-edge. Our neighbours are staying in refugee camps: it's squalid and miserable. I don't want my family begging to scrounge one miserable plate of rice."

"What about your uncle in Burma? I was there 10 years ago. Why can't we go to Rangoon?"

"You don't understand, I've written to Burma twice already. My uncle never replied, so he might not be in any position to help us. You need to realise the truth: people are afraid we'd be a burden."

"I still think that it is better to go to Calcutta rather than the village," Grandmother persisted.

There was a long pause. "It is not an easy journey from Chittagong to Calcutta. You are not as fit as before. I have to think about you and Mrinal. Can you both walk for long distances – could you run if you had to, through the jungle?"

Still, the grandmother was not happy with the decision to go to the village.

They put everything in their Morris Minor. It was jam-packed inside the car. From their city house to the village was thirty miles and used to take three hours in those days. That night, however, they started at ten o'clock. and didn't reach in the village until four in the morning. The roads were blocked at several locations, with military checkpoints set up every five miles, and Sumana's little brother was crying throughout the journey. Aunt Lila told Sumana to shut her eyes and sleep but she still saw the dead bodies in the ditches, their hands tied behind their backs, killed by close-range fire.

For Sumana and her siblings during the war, village life offered little variety. They ate, slept and enjoyed occasional activities with Aunt Lila, like drawing or sewing. Every night before going to sleep, Aunt Lila, Sumana's mother and the grandmother dressed themselves in the petticoats that held the sewn-in gold. They were prepared to run at a moment's notice, with coals and ashes kept ready to daub on their faces to disguise their appearance. If the Pakistani army came overnight, women would dirty their faces and hide in the paddy fields. The key of the Morris Minor was kept visible by the front door, so the army could find it easily and would not set fire to the car.

It was not comfortable staying in the village: their house had no inside toilet, nor shower. The family had to take their bath in the pond. Still, Sumana was happy because she did not have to go to school – moreover, she could play with her Uncle Badal. She liked Uncle Badal more than Uncle Sajal because Badal was very energetic, playing basketball and football with her, and teaching her to ride a bicycle. Together they would try to catch fish from the village ponds. By contrast, Uncle Sajal, who was a hospital intern, was always in a serious mood. However, on several occasions as they headed back from the fields and chatted to acquaintances as they walked home through the bazaar, Sumana noticed that even Uncle Badal could become very tense.

Sumana's father commuted daily from the village to his office in Chittagong city in the Morris Minor. He left early in every morning and returned late at night. Her grandmother and Sumana's mother would pray all day for his safe return. They were relieved when he got home. Sumana's father was very tall, handsome and fair with a full head of hair and an aristocratic moustache, and spoke English and Urdu. His appearance and language skills led Pakistani Army officers on several occasions to mistake him for a police officer when demanding a lift from him. His calm and gentle demeanour rescued him in this difficult situation.

One evening, Sumana returned late from playing.

Aunt Lila had been looking for her: "Sumana, you are not opening your books at all. You will forget all your maths and English grammar and translation."

Sumana answered promptly: "I will open my books and do some maths after dinner."

"We are not allowed to light the lamp after sunset anymore."

Sumana asked: "Do we have to stay in the dark all night?"

"Yes. The Pakistani Military are coming close. The village chief has requested that everyone should switch off their electric lights and leave the kerosene lamps unlit at night. This way, the army will not be able to find their way to the village and will be unable to shell us from the distance."

From that day, they ate before sunset and then sat together in front of the radio with a single candle in the middle of the room.

One day Sumana's father returned from the city with a colleague whose wife and little boy stayed with them until the war finished. Her grandmother asked Sumana's father, "Why have you bought them? We are living on rice, vegetables and dahl. They are Muslims: they eat meat most of the time. We are in no situation to entertain them now."

Her father replied, "They are in great danger. It's not safe for them in the city, and they cannot go back to their own village: it is over three hundred and sixty miles to Nilphamari. They are happy to share whatever we eat. Please, Mother, be kind and considerate to them."

The little boy in that family was seven years old and named Sohag. Sumana could not play with Sohag because they spoke in different dialects: only Aunt Lila could communicate well with Sohag's mother. The family stayed in their room all day and only joined Sumana's at mealtimes.

One night, Sumana was awaken by a loud altercation between Uncle Badal and her father.

Uncle Badal was insisting: "I am going to join the Mukti Bahini." This was a guerrilla band of Bangladeshi freedom fighters.

Sumana's father shouted angrily: "You b***rd, you contribute nothing to this family. Mukti Bahini doesn't even have any bullets to fight the Pakistani Army!"

"The Indian army is providing training and ammunition."

"Don't believe that bulls**t, you have zero chance of winning this war."

"Bangubondhu Sheikh Mujibor Rahman has called our whole nation to join the war and fight against the Pakistani Army. Haven't you heard his speech 'This time the struggle is for our freedom'?"

"For goodness' sake! My office is being run by the Pakistani government. We all depend on my earnings. I'd be prosecuted if anyone from the office found out that my brother joined the Mukti Bahini."

Uncle Badal answered: "The Pakistan government has deprived and coerced us in every sector. Don't be so vain: the rice we eat comes from our own paddy field. We can do without your salary. I know you'll lose your job if anyone finds out about me, but if you are so ashamed of my joining the Mukti Bahini then just don't tell anyone that your brother is a Bengali guerrilla fighter."

Sumana's grandmother was weeping. "Please Badal, listen to me," she said. "Stop quarrelling. This is pointless. War, murder, fighting – they are not our way. We are a simple family. Let the big people take the big steps. Why are you punishing me? Why do you want to break my heart? Please, I beg you."

Badal replied, after a long pause: "I understand you, Mother. It just seems wrong to sit at home and enjoy life while this war is going on. I feel guilty when every conscientious person is joining the Mukti Bahini and trying to fight against the Pakistani army."

Grandmother said: "We all are suffering."

Badal said: "Forgive me, mother, but I can't ignore my country's call. I leave in the morning."

Sumana's grandmother, mother and Aunt Lila spent the whole night crying and trying to dissuade him but, next morning, Badal left to fight for the Bangladesh Liberation War.

Sumana was very upset and missed her boisterous Uncle Badal. Her grandmother wept all day long, searching the house for a photograph of Badal, praying and refusing to touch any food. The whole house was silent. No-one in the house apart from Badal knew how to tune the radio properly so it made strange noises all day on every channel: BBC Bangla, The Voice of America, Betar Bangladesh… From that day, the grandmother stopped listening to the radio because she was so upset about her son. Aunt Lila and Sumana's mother would take the radio outside to try to find better reception.

One night, Sumana was awakened by her father returning late from the office. He had been stopped by the Pakistani military and asked to recite from the Quran. He had managed to charm his way out of danger, somehow talking the officer round. But Sumana's grandmother was very worried and invited the Buddhist monks from the village over the next day to say special prayers. Uncle Sajal also came to visit them from his hospital accommodation.

The head monk said: "We have good relations with the Pakistani army. As you know, China is supporting Pakistan in this war. We have introduced ourselves as Chinese Buddhists. Thanks to this camouflage, we can survive the military invasion."

Aunt Lila asked: "Should monks get involved in politics?"

Her grandmother and Uncle Sajal, told Lila to keep quiet and not ask any more questions.

But the head monk replied: "We are not directly involved in politics. Due to the presence of the Buddhist temple, the army did not set fire to this village."

He continued: "I heard Badal left for the Mukti Bahini."

Sumana's grandmother begged: "Please do not tell anyone about Badal."

The head monk reassured her: "Don't worry, I won't. I will arrange a Chinese Buddhist pass for your son to ensure him safe passage every day from his office to the village."

The head monk asked, "Doctor Sajal, do you need a pass as well? I can provide one for you."

Uncle Sajal answered quietly, "No, I do not need one."

After the monks had left, Uncle Sajal was furious with his mother for inviting them, shouting: "Buddhist monks should not get involved in politics. 'Good relations with the Pakistani army.' How dare they? What an audacity! Since when did we become Chinese? We have been Bengalis for fourteen generations! With the support the Indian army and Indira Gandhi are giving Mutki Bahini now, there's every chance that the Pakistani army will meet their defeat." He paused to catch his breath. "When they do, you can believe these monks and so-called 'Chinese Buddhists' will switch their camouflage again. But mark my words: the days of Pakistani dominance are numbered."

Sumana's father was speechless and he did not open his mouth even though he did not support Sajal's opinion. Everyone in the family was frightened of Sajal's views and intimated by Sajal's extreme sense of justice.

This significant foresight of Uncle Sajal about the war worried everyone. At the dining table, there was another hot discussion. Lunch was served: rice, dahl and vegetables.

Sajal stared. "No fish curry? No eggs?"

The grandmother answered sheepishly: "No Sajal. This is what we eat now. You can see how many mouths we have to feed every day."

Sajal gestured to Sumana and her siblings. "Without protein these children will be malnourished!"

The grandmother said: "The price of fish is so high."

Sajal left the village that evening in an aggressive mood. He gave the grandmother cash to buy fish for dinner. Everyone was relieved when the grave Sajal had gone.

Sumana was in a dilemma that night.

She asked Aunt Lila: "Did Uncle Badal make the best choice in joining the Mukti Bahinis?"

Aunt Lila shrugged. "I don't know."

She continued: "If Uncle Sajal is correct and the Mukti Bahinis win freedom, will the monks and my father be in trouble for not supporting the war?"

"I cannot answer now. Only time will tell. Remember, your father, the monks, all of us support the war. But to survive this precarious situation requires diplomacy." She sighed. "The war is too complex for easy explanations, and you are too young to understand it. Now it is time to sleep."

One day father came from the city early with the rumour that Mukti Bahini had annihilated the Pakistani army.

Overjoyed, he shouted: "Lila, quick – sew Bangladesh flags!"

Sumana's father sat glued to the radio all that day – but the rumour had been wrong. The Pakistani army seemed in fact to be gaining power, thanks to ammunition sent from China and the United States of America. Her father ordered Sumana and Lila to burn all their flags.

Soon after, in December 1971 came the news that a USA convoy named Task Force 74 from the Seventh Fleet of the US Navy was being deployed by President Nixon to the Bay of Bengal.

On 14th December 1971 Bangladeshi professors, doctors, architects, journalists, engineers and writers were killed overnight in the grounds of Dhaka University. The Pakistani army wanted to cripple our nation: not only through genocide and rape, but also by destroying those who held its collective knowledge and wisdom.

Her grandmother was worried that there was no word from Badal. She was also thinking of Uncle Sajal, knowing that doctors were targets for the army too. A man arrived from the city, breathless with sad news. A distant relative, an engineer in Chittagong City, had been seized by the Army and killed in front of his family. Mercifully, the army officers did not rape his wife and did not take away the family to the army camp.

On 16th December 1971, the Pakistani army under Lt Gen Niazi surrendered all ammunitions to Lt Gen Jagjit Singh Arora, Commander-in-Chief of the Indian Army, the Mukti Bahini and newly formed Bangladesh Forces in Ramna Racecourse Maydan. Bangladesh had won victory in the war for liberation.

Sumana's father did not go to the office, sitting beside the radio again all that day. Aunt Lila was again busy making flags for Bangladesh. A new nation was born: a free country, free from Pakistan's exploitation, from its army's brutality and from the stress of war.

Nine months later, Sumana and her family returned to their house in Chittagong city. The thatched part of the house had been destroyed by fire but the brick half had survived. The furniture was still smouldering. Everyone wept to see the damage done by the Pakistani army and their collaborators, the Rajakars.

Uncle Sajal arrived to help them organise everything. Sifting through the ashes, Sumana found her charred drawing book, with the drawing of the fires on the horizon, mirroring the current state of her house. Aunt Lila was crying over her school certificates, all burned now. The grandmother was screaming for her son Badal, still missing, clutching a photo of him from a family album. Sumana's mother and Uncle Sajal comforted her as Sumana's younger brother and sister started to play with their burnt toys.

Sumana's father had bought packets of sweets in this situation because the Mukti Bahini had won in the liberation war and he wanted to celebrate the victory of Bangladesh.

Sumana felt sad that Uncle Badal was not there to share their joy. She remembered her father's pessimism and uncertainty about the war; his exasperation with Uncle Badal for joining the Mukti Bahini. Sumana had a conflict in her mind as to why her father was distributing the sweets while he had not himself won anything. She was also anxious that, in the future, the behaviour of her father and the head monk might appear hypocritical and duplicitous. She did not yet realise that her concern would fade with the memories of the conflict, the defeated Pakistani army and their collaborative Rajakars, in a whole nation's collective historical amnesia.

Freedom

It was my wedding night. It had been a gorgeous day, with a grand ceremony and reception arranged by my parents. Approximately twelve hundred people had attended with my friends, my sister's friends, my parents' friends and colleagues, and all our extended family were among the guests. It was a night in late winter and the temperature was very comfortable, around eighteen to twenty degrees. I was dressed in a maroon sari with heavy embroidery and I wore three gold necklaces – one from my parents, one from my in-laws and one from my auntie – along with heavy gold earrings, twelve gold bangles and one gold tiara. The top beautician in the city had been appointed to decorate me with heavy makeup to disguise my dark skin colour. My hair was arranged with fresh flowers and glitter. My hands and palms were painted with Mehdi.

The complete costume was extremely uncomfortable. I was not excited, but anxious. These clothes and ornaments had been chosen to display to the invited guests the status of both families. The dinner was another conscious display of our family's wealth, with catering by a top chef, and the reception arranged in one of the most expensive venues in the city. It was a family tradition and everyone had to comply with this arrangement. Our relatively conservative parents did not consider arranging an open-air concert, the latest trend among our society. Still, everything ran according to plan, and my family handed me over to my new husband's. It was incredibly sad: my family knew their daughter was leaving forever. Marriage is perceived as a one-way ticket to captivity. I didn't cry out loud, but I wept bitterly inside.

That night, my husband asked: "Are you feeling okay?"

Despite not feeling all right with the heavy dress and ornaments in a new environment, I replied: "OK."

"What can I give you, what do you want from me?"

Without hesitation my answer burst out of me: "Freedom."

"You will not be a prisoner in our family."

I sighed. "Today I am imprisoned in this dress and these ornaments, from tomorrow I will feel shackled within the rules and regulations of this family. I want freedom."

My husband asked what I meant by the word.

"I would like to have the freedom to go to my parents' house whenever I want, the freedom to speak the truth, to call my friends, the freedom to enjoy nature, to stand up for the people who need my help, and I need the freedom to read and write whatever I like."

"Your demands are very high," my husband said. "You might not get all of that here."

Within a week of our marriage, my uncle died. It was not a good omen to cross the river within a week of a marriage so I was not allowed to go to his funeral. I was permitted to see my uncle's body in the city but I didn't go to the village. I did not cry or argue with my in-laws, but I could already feel the shackles on my legs. A couple of days later, a friend phoned; I was very excited and started to speak loudly. My in-laws objected to this: asking me not to speak or laugh loudly and in future to subdue my voice. Our house had a flat roof where I used to enjoy walking and singing on moonlit nights but I was no longer allowed to sing at night. I was told off for feeding birds and animals, as I'd loved to do. They said it was a waste of food.

After all these experiences, I stopped reading and writing. The ink in my Parker was as dry as my brain. I forgot how to write, how to enjoy a good book or even how to enjoy good weather. I didn't visit the shanty town and never bought food for the poor.

I have been married for 20 years now. I have surrendered my life, my hope, my expectations. Not a single request from my wedding night was granted. I now believe that "Freedom is slavery". I'm not a strong person: this marriage changed me, keeping me subservient, robbing me of the courage to fight for release. I am crawling as a worm in the world. I was moulded by circumstances and embraced peace with slavery.

The people of Bangladesh gained their liberation twice, once from British rule and then from the exploitation by Pakistan. Our coveted and hard-earned freedom did not bring female emancipation. My country's history has taught me that peace and the fight for liberation cannot go hand in hand. In order to lead a peaceful life, I have sacrificed my desire to be free.

Pohela Boishakh

Bengali New Year's day is known as Pohela Boishakh. The year starts in the summer month of Boishakh. From India to Vietnam, most of the nations celebrate New Years's Day in the month of April according to the lunar calendar. Different countries call the celebration by different names: in Sri Lanka, Puthandu; in Myanmar, Thingyan; in Thailand, Songkran; in Laos, Pi Mai; in Cambodia, Chaul Chnam Thmey; and in China, Poshuijie. In Kolkata and Bangladesh, New Year's Day is known as Pohela Boishakh.

In the Bengali community it is a huge part of our culture and heritage, and we take it very seriously. Celebrations start the day before, as the old year turns into the new. Everything in the house – furniture, utensils, curtains, floors – is subjected to a deep clean. A bonfire is lit to burn the insects, diseases, old leaves, bad habits and bad karma, and we chant in Chittagong:

Jag jag jag
Aoro barit jag
Taeha poisha sona ruha aoro barit jag
Jak jak jak
Rog, bedhi jak
dorijar khulodi jak

The heat, glow and crackle of the fire annihilate the old diseases and evil spirits and bring happiness and prosperity for the year to come. The last day of the year finishes with a bitter curry and we chew bitter leaves from the neem tree to purify the bowels.

The next morning our houses are decorated with flowers and leaves from the neem tree. Bengalis put on new clothes, pray for a prosperous year, greet each other with "Shuvo Nababarsha!" (Happy New Year) and distribute sweets and good food, hoping for better days ahead. Businessmen open new ledgers for the new financial year. Everyone enjoys it in their own way. In the villages, open markets sell handicrafts and local products. In Chittagong, the famous "Jabbar Alir Bolikhela", a wrestling competition, is a great attraction. In recent years, art students in the big cities have arranged carnivals with colourful paper masks and papier mâché sculptures celebrating Bengali culture. All over Bangladesh, in cities, towns and even villages, local performers give open-air concerts.

Rahela and Malati decided to make that New Year special in Ramna Uddan. As graduating students, they might not be in Dhaka next year, so they treated themselves to white saris with red fringes and red blouses. They chose flowers for their hair from the florists in Shahbagh and even remembered to get Kodak film for their cameras. On New Year's Day, they woke up early. In their elegant new clothes and with white flowers, they looked very pretty.

Several times on their journey, they saw a single myna bird in different locations. A solitary myna is a sinister omen and counted as "one for sorrow."

Malati finally remarked: "'One for sorrow' again! I'm getting worried. Something bad is sure to happen today."

Rahela said: "I cannot believe that you are still superstitious. Nothing will go wrong, we will be okay." To change the conversation she continued: "Do you know who's performing at the concert this morning?"

Malati only said: "It's my first time. I'd much rather avoid the crowds. I'm only going because you persuaded me."

"We have to enjoy Pohela Boishakh this year – next year who knows where we will be? Are my flowers ok? These hairpins are really uncomfortable."

"Perfect. You look like the Goddess Durga. Let's walk fast, though, before it gets hot and crowded. We're already late – we might not get chance to sit near the stage."

They saw a float carrying the papier-mâché sculpture of the Royal Bengal Tiger coming towards them. Rahela asked a stranger: "Would you please take a photo of us with the tiger?"

The stranger took a picture and they thanked him.

Rahela was very excited, but Malati still looked anxious.

Rahela said: "Malati, smile, I'm taking your picture! You can't blame me if you don't look pretty."

Another float passed them carrying a sculpture of a dragon. This time Rahela could not find a cooperative stranger to take their pictures, so they photographed each other next to the dragon.

They stopped by a vendor selling Fuska (small deep-fried flatbread filled with a mixture of mashed potatoes, onions, chickpeas, tarmarind chutney and chilli powder) and Chotpoti (a dish of chickpeas, potatoes and onions topped with diced chilli, grated boiled eggs, cumin, coriander leaves and tarmarind chutney). They ordered a plate of each, with extra-hot sauce.

The vendor said: "Apa," – a traditional address for young girls – "Come back this afternoon, and I will serve you a special New Year's dish: Panta Bhat (rice soaked in water), Fried Hilsha (the national fish of Bangladesh) and Alu Bharta (mashed potatoes)."

Rahela said: "We don't know what time we will be coming back. We can't promise you but we will try. Your chotpoti is the best."

While they were crossing Shaheed Meenar (the national monument for Language Martyrs), they saw Sabuj , one of their classmates. He was wearing a punjabi, the national dress of Bengalis.

He said: "I have never seen you in a sari before. You both look stunning."

They glowed pink with embarrassment, although it could not be seen because of their thick foundation.

Rahela said: "No need to flatter us. Just help us take some pictures in front of the Shaheed Meenar."

Malati protested: "Don't use it all up! We've already taken so many."

Sabuj checked the film counter. "Twenty-five... You've still got eleven left."

After taking their photos, they started to walk towards the Ramna Uddan.

They reached the concert venue in good time. They were just taking their places and felt lucky to have found spaces near the stage. All of a sudden, they saw the crowd was moving towards the main entrance. Someone had tossed a bomb at the performance stage and it exploded. All the musical instruments were scattered, the performers quickly fled for their lives and the stage was ransacked.

Malati desperately grabbed hold of Rahela's hand as together they tried to run. But before they knew what was happening, another bomb had gone off, throwing them to the ground. For a moment Malati lay blinded, unable to see Rahela. As her vision cleared again, she spotted her: Rahela had been tossed some distance by the force of the explosion. She lay crumpled and bloodsoaked, her white sari dirty and red, her flowers black with ash and mud. One of her hands had been ripped off by the blast: it lay alongside her body, its fingers still reaching out as if clutching for Malati's. Malati stared but could not comprehend what had happened. The area was flooded with blood, strewn with scattered body parts. She was still sitting, dumbfounded, when Sabuj appeared at her side. Together they were taken to hospital.

Ramna Uddan looked like a vision of hell. Crying and screaming filled the air. Volunteers rushed to help as ambulances and police cars arrived. Ten people had been killed in the bombing. Malati, who had been filled with a sense of foreboding on seeing the solitary myna bird, was discharged with only minor injuries. She could still hear Rahela's voice, happy and unconcerned: "We have to enjoy Pohela Boishakh this year – next year who knows where we will be?"

Malati never again joined in with the New Year celebrations.

The cultural program of Bangladesh was set back in 2001 as the perpetrators were successful in stopping the Pohela Boishakh in Bangladesh but they were unable to stop the celebrations in neighbouring countries. New Year's Day was still celebrated throughout South East Asia under its many different names. The bombing at the beginning of the year threatened to mark the end of an era for the nation. The assault on Pohela Boishakh struck Bangladesh full in the face and delivered a massive blow to its identity and heritage. Bangladesh still faces a test of endurance.

Kaptai Barrage

One of our favourite day trips was to Kaptai Lake, a popular spot for school and college picnics, two-hours' drive from Chittagong City. This lake is very beautiful: a huge stretch of turquoise blue water surrounded by lush, green woodland. We liked to hire a boat and would happily explore for hours, visiting Chakma Rajar Bari (the Palace of Chakma Raja), Rajbon Bihar (the Royal Buddhist Temple), the Hanging Bridge, and the Chingmorom Buddhist Temple, which nestled among the mountains on the other side of the river.

The only problem was that we had to return to Chittagong before nightfall as the road to the city was dark and difficult. It was also dangerous, because the Shanti Bahini (a tribal peacekeeping force) was very hostile to Bengalis and might attack us in the dark, so we were always in a hurry to get home. Our journey crossed a couple of Bangladeshi military checkpoints before entering the Chittagong Hill Tracts, and no foreigners were allowed through without special permission.

The boatman, the shopkeepers and the hawkers belonged to tribes who spoke very little Bangla and whose dress, language, culture and food were different from ours. Whether they hated us or were scared of us we could not tell, but they always kept themselves to themselves and were never openly friendly.

I once tried to chat with a boatman, but he was reluctant to reply, though he was happily murmuring to himself throughout the trip – at least until his wife, bailing out the water, shouted at him to stop. His wife had an enormous bun of hair with prominent cheeks and wrinkled skin.

Spotting her locket from the Golden Buddhist Temple (Shwedagon Pagoda) of Myanmar, I grabbed my chance:

"Mashi," using the polite title for a middle-aged woman, "Your locket is very pretty. Have you been to Myanmar?"

"No, Didi," the usual title for a young girl. "We cannot afford to go to Myanmar. We do not even have enough money to visit Chittagong. This locket was given to me by the head monk from the Chingmorom Buddhist Temple."

"We have just visited that temple and met the monk today. He is very kind and has given us some fruit and biscuits. Would you like some?" I offered.

"No, Didi, I have had my breakfast and am not hungry now."

I ventured: "You're so lucky, getting to enjoy this beautiful scenery every day."

She paused. "The area was more beautiful before the dam was built."

Becoming more talkative now, she introduced herself as Nioti Chakma. She said her husband was not in good health and had not spoken much since the night the lake took his voice away. I expressed astonishment that this tranquil lake could deprive someone of the power of speech. Nioti then told me the full story.

The Kaptai Lake is known to the tribal people as the 'Lake of Tears': one night in 1961 the lake stole houses, farmlands, schools, playgrounds and bazaars; drowning their entire world. The lake is man-made and was formed when the Karnaphuli River was dammed for an American-funded hydro-electric plant that would generate electricity for Chittagong and the surrounding region.

Nioti and her husband, Bimal were from a farming village producing rice and other crops. Bimal managed to earn a good living from the land, which was very fertile. But the creation of the lake left their entire community homeless and destitute. Nioti and her husband moved to an empty tract of land the other side of the hill, where they managed to build themselves a shed to live in, but they had lost their livelihood. The government compensation did not extend to their family or to their community due to bureaucracy and corruption. Starving, they tried to get help from the 'Chakma Raja' – the hereditary chief of their ethnic group – but he was in no position to help, as his own palace was now under water. All he could offer was consolation and reassurance. The promised government resettlement never materialised and a large number of people left for India and became refugees. Bimal and his family did not leave, because they did not want an uncertain life in India.

The village people gathered together to find a solution. Deciding to protest against the injustice done to them, the tribes united to rebel. Forming groups like Shanti Bahini, which Bimal's son and nephew had joined, the tribes were still fighting the Government for compensation for their land.

Farming had been Bimal's only trade. With no other skills to draw on, he borrowed money from the leader of the tribe and bought a boat. The income from the boat provided them with food but life was not easy. Bimal's son had died in a fight between the Bangladeshi army and the Shanti Bahini. Now, every morning and evening, Bimal goes to the Chingmorom Temple and prays to Buddha for his blessing that "one day the Karnafuli River will dry up or the dam will be destroyed by natural calamities, and that my son will come back." Outside the temple, he talks very little and murmurs when not in prayer. He curses his fate and hates the lake.

I was saddened to hear their story. The joyful boat trip no longer gave me any pleasure. Staring out at the water of the lake, serene and turquoise blue, I felt the gentle breeze was whispering something that I could not understand. It seemed to carry the voices of a distant crowd wailing for life – though whether I sensed or only imagined it, I could not tell. We returned home with heavy hearts. Since that day, I have only returned to visit the Temple.

I cannot appreciate the beauty of the lake now; the gentle breeze, or that wild cry, has stirred my conscience.

Invasion

My name is Chelly Prue Marma. Our village is in the district of Bandarban in the Chittagong Hill Tracts, the mountainous area where I was born. The Shangu River flows straight through our 'para' – our name for a hamlet of houses – and we used its water for all our household work: bathing and doing our laundry there, and fetching the water in pails for cooking, or to clean our homes. It is not deep: it is a rafting river. Every new year we would enjoy the Sangrai Festival – a water festival which took place on the riverbanks.

A couple of mountain streams ran steadily throughout the year in this area. It was quiet and serene. We heard the sound of running water and birdsong all day long, and by moonlight the streams glistened. We lived a simple but happy life. Early every morning, I would travel to Keyang, the Buddhist temple, for Morning Prayers, leaving for school at ten o'clock. When I returned at half past three, I would help my mother with the housework, and after dinner we would spin cotton and weave the fabric for our clothes.

My mother worked all day in the forest in a method of agriculture known generally as 'shifting cultivation' and locally as 'Jhum Chash'. This traditional method of farming has been practised by indigenous tribes for centuries: after one harvest, we move on and clear another small area of forest. My mother would leave early in the morning, taking my little sister on her back. She collected wood and weeded the cultivated area, caught fish from the river or hunted forest animals.

One day she found a baby deer, a faun, and brought it home. It was beautiful with light spotted fur and was shy and gentle. We built a small shed to prevent its escape: it is said that a deer is a good omen and brings harmony and abundance. We looked after it well, but it died unexpectedly during the rainy season, from snakebite. After the deer's death, we suffered a year of bad harvests. Another time, my mother captured a small monkey in the forest. We kept him in the shed, where he would howl noisily every night, but during the day he was playful and would join in games with me and my sister. I loved to cuddle him. After only a few weeks, however, he started to throw faeces at everyone. Our neighbours said he was stressed from captivity, so my mother decided to release him back into the forest. She used to catch hedgehogs – for food, not as pets – but the amount of meat was barely enough to feed us. When she hunted wild pigs, though, it was always an exciting day and we would feast.

Marma society is matrilineal. My mother attended to everything in our family, from forest farming to caring for our home. My father didn't work; most of the time he drank rice wine. For jhum cultivation, my mother burned the remnants of the previous year's harvest, prepared fresh ground for cultivation and planted the new area with seeds. We harvested papayas, bananas, pineapples, chillies, sticky rice, garlic, onions and many other vegetables. Our territories spanned all Banderban: we did not have boundaries or legal documents for our land. We believe the Marma Raja, our king, owns the land: he is a good ruler, and his family is kind to us. The best harvest is presented to the Raja's house in his honour.

In 1980, the Bangladesh government began settling Bengalis in this region, building them houses here. People from different parts of the country, especially flood victims, were settled in the villages of Guchuugram. Many people migrated to our village, spelling the end of our traditional way of life. There was a mass eviction of many natives, significantly shifting the ethnic demographics. The lowland people showed no respect for our law and culture, despising our food, lacking any connection to nature, polluting the rivers and forests. Woodlands were burnt down without care to make room for houses. The serenity of our lands was disturbed by noise. Without formal documents proving our rights to the land, we were overrun by settlers. They destroyed our habitat and that of the forest animals. We were deprived of our livelihood.

Our traditional dress is different from the Bengalis'; men wear trousers and women wear saris. The Marma wear sarongs: men wear the lungi while the women have thami, with colourful blouses. The Bengali women, being Muslim, wear headscarves, but our women don't suffer those restrictions to their freedom. Differences like these stoked the conflict between the tribes and the settlers.

Like me, my younger sister used to attend high school. On her way home one day, one of the settlers' boys ordered her to cover her head with a scarf. She answered back, telling him to mind his own business, but the boy and with his friends wouldn't leave her alone, verbally abusing her in front of her companions. Our community took it very seriously: there was chaos in the village that night. The following week my sister was abducted on her way to school. We found her mutilated corpse in the Shangu River.

When my father went to the police, they refused to take up the case. The officers blamed the Marma boys for starting the trouble by threatening the settlers. They said that, in any case, my sister had received the appropriate punishment for refusing to wear a head scarf. We cried and complained but no case was filed.

The settlers have occupied most of our land. And now that our Raja has died, and his family has left for Myanmar or India, the settlers have asked the Marma to leave the Chittagong Hill Tracts. They say that Bangladesh is for Bengalis only, not for tribal communities. This has been our home for centuries – where can we go? My mother is eighty now: too old to work farming the forest, though she still weaves clothes and blankets to sell on the souvenir market.

They have decided to build a holiday resort here. The government says it will help to boost the economy of the region, our people will get jobs and our standard of life will be improved. I am dubious. A resort will destroy even more farmland and forest. Without high-up contacts it is proving hard to find jobs as tourist guides – only one of my cousins has managed it. With so many people coming to holiday here, our land is becoming overpopulated, its calm and tranquillity obliterated. It starts with one resort but you can bet there soon will be a dozen more. We have lost our land, culture and religion. There has been no support for our fight for survival against greed and commercialism.

Recently I watched a documentary about how the Europeans invaded the lands of the Native Americans and Aboriginal Australians centuries ago. A similar incident happened in Bangladesh in the last 50 years. Across the world, indigenous peoples are the most disadvantaged communities. History repeats itself again and again but we overlook it. I believe that one day we will win back our lands and our forests but that will be too late for compensation, even for Mother Nature.

Conversion

At six o'clock on a winter's morning, Manilal returned from the river with a good catch. He was a fisherman on the River Shitalakha. The fishermen were Hindus. Manilal had offered prayers to Lakshmi, the Goddess of wealth, before going to the river, and was satisfied with that morning's haul. He thanked Lakshmi from the bottom of his heart and decided to offer a special prayer after returning home. The middleman Abdullah was a shrewd broker: his trick was to buy insufficient blocks of ice to force the fishermen to accept a lower price if they wanted their catch kept cold.

Manilal haggled with him over an hour: he did not want to sell at Abdullah's price but he could not see another middleman in the Ghat. Eventually, in frustration, Manilal punched Abdullah, hired a van and started off for the town. Although hiring the van was not cheap, he could earn more money if he got there before the auction. Manilal arrived in time and did indeed secure himself a better price from the fish trader. He was very happy, buying some groceries for his family and new clothes for his youngest son, a toddler, though he could not buy any clothes for his wife, his mother, his two other sons and two teenage daughters. Instead, he bought sweets from the town for the rest of his family. He was happy that Abdullah hadn't managed to cheat him this time, but he was to pay a high price for his audacity.

That night, he was awakened by a deafening cry from his wife, Jaba, screaming: "Fire! Fire! Run!"

Flames engulfed the thatched roof, sidewall, wooden door and bedding. Manilal's Lakshmi idol was already on fire and burned immediately. He pulled his two sons and two daughters from their beds and ordered them to wait in front of the hut. He could not fight his way back in, so his eighty-year-old mother was left in the house. Jaba, searching for their toddler, was also trapped inside – someone pulled her out but she collapsed, falling to the ground, her sari catching fire. She died from her burns. The roof of the house collapsed on the bed where the old mother and the toddler were lying. People gathered with buckets of water from ponds and wells but that was not enough to put out the fire. The dry winter leaves spread the fire to the next-door neighbour's house.

That night, Manilala lost his mother, his youngest son, his wife and his shelter. Everyone in the village knew Abdullah had set fire to Manilal's house in order to teach the fishermen a lesson, so that they would not argue with him or overrule his price. Abdullah went into hiding and would not be seen in the neighbourhood for the next couple of months.

Imam Nazim came from the mosque to help the fishermen. Manilal had never liked him much due to his talkativeness but Nazim offered them shelter next to the mosque. Except Manilal, no other neighbours accompanied the Imam toward the mosque. He followed the Imam, his two sons and two daughters silently walking behind.

"How can best I help you, Manilal?" said Imam Nazim.

Manilal could not answer; for a while he was speechless.

"You have to be strong, and pray to Allah," the Imam continued. "He can save you. You have to survive for these motherless boys and girls."

Manilal did not have enough energy to reply to Imam and had no stamina left to fight Abdullah. He was perplexed, he did not know how to look after these children alone. He could not understand how he could live without his mother, his wife, his youngest son and his home. His fishing nets had been burned and he had lost his livelihood. He was desperate to put right the injustice done to him but he was powerless.

Manilal began to wail and curse his destiny.

"Do not cry; do not shed tears, Manilal. The world has not stopped tonight. I will help you to build a hut and to look after the children," Imam Nazim reassured.

Nothing could stop Manilal. He continued weeping.

The father, sons and daughters spent the next couple of nights sleeping under the stars, the Imam supplying them with food. They remained outside the mosque, as none of them were permitted to enter, not being Muslims.

The Imam advised Manilal to convert to Islam. "If you do, I can help you. Your sons and daughters can go the Madrasah (Islamic school). They'll get three meals a day and the best Islamic education."

Manilal could not think at all and replied with a deep sigh: "I do not know what to do with these children. Huzur, please help me."

Imam Nazim was also addressed as Huzur, another word for priest.

"My suggestion is that you convert. Until then, I am not able to help you."

"I am worthless, Huzur; please, help me and my children."

"Allah will help you," Imam Nazim reassured. "Not I."

Manilal took the name Motaleb Mia and was converted to Islam after following all the rituals. His sons and daughters were given new names as well. They were happy as they got new clothes and packets of beef biryani and sweets. His two sons were sent to the Madrasha with the hope of having three meals a day. The daughters did not get the opportunity yet as the female Madrasha had no places for that session but at least Manilal had two fewer mouths to feed. Imam Nazim had assisted Manilal to build a new shed just beside the mosque.

It rained heavily during that monsoon. Manilal's daughters couldn't cook any food for two days as the hobs got wet, so they all had to survive on dried chira (puffed rice). Manilal could not go fishing as the river swelled into dangerously high tides during the rainy season. He could only linger in their little hut, with no money to buy anything from the nearby shops. Imam Nazim came with a plastic sheet to protect the hobs from getting wet. He was dressed in fresh white clothes and had put on some attar (perfume) and surma (eyeliner). His beard was dyed with Mehdi. Next to Imam Nazim's finery, Manilal's hut looked even more pitiable.

Imam Nazim spoke, emphasising his new name: "How are you Motaleb? I thought the rain might have become a problem, so I bought you a plastic sheet."

Manilal said: "You have done a lot for me, I am grateful for your help, Huzur."

"I did not do much, it was all done by Allah. Where are your daughters? I'm sorry I was not able to send them to the Madrasah; I'm hopeful they'll be enrolled by next year."

Calling for his daughters, Manilal cried: "Namita, Sabita," using the names they had been originally called, rather than their Muslim names 'Julekha' and 'Jahanara'. "Where are you? Come and offer some chira to our guest."

The Imam chided Manilal for using the girls' old names.

"We are at home," Manilal objected. "Nobody's listening. I can call my daughters what I like."

Imam Nazim said: "You should not do that; it is not good in the eye of Islam."

Sabita, the younger daughter, came in with a plate of chira.

The Imam seemed disappointed. He said, "I was looking for Julekha, your elder girl. I have some good news: I have got a marriage proposal for her."

Manilal said: "So, who would want the daughter of a poor man? Who's the bridegroom?"

Imam Nazim answered with a big smile: "I would like to marry her. Although I am fifty years old, I am asking to be the bridegroom for your teenage daughter." He continued: "She will be happy in my house and will enjoy the company of my three other wives."

Manilal was dumbstruck. He and his daughter knew all too well what the consequences of declining the proposal would be. And so teenage Namita was married to the fifty-year-old Imam Nazim the following Friday. Manilal was not asked to provide a dowry for his daughter. Imam is blessed by Allah as he has now four Bibis (wives).

Imam Nazim was delighted with Manilal. Thanks to this poor fisherman, he could fulfil all the necessary criteria for becoming a good Muslim: he'd converted five people to Islam, enrolled new madrasah students and, last but not least, he now had a fourth wife who was a teenager. Certainly, he was sure, he would reach Jannat (heaven) as soon as he took his final breath.

Manilal could never find much time for reflection: in poverty, you're more concerned with your next meal. Philosophising and debating the values of different religions is a luxury, a big topic for big people. Manilal only cares about putting food in his mouth and tries to avoid hunger; he does not care whether he is called as "Manilal" or "Motaleb".

Monasteries Burning

It was on the stroke of midnight, 29th of September, 2012, that the monasteries were set on fire. Orange flames glowed and gleamed in the night sky, turning the Bangladesh skyline into a vision of Hell. The country was awakened to ultimate truth and experienced a glimpse of barbarity. The perpetrators were charging around, shouting "Allah-hu-Akbar, God is great" in the streets. The cause of the outrage that had resulted in the fire had been an allegedly derogatory image of a partially-burnt copy of the Quran, which had circulated on Facebook. Clearly, human thought processes have not benefited from our advances in science and technology.

The thatched roofs of the monasteries had caught fire immediately. To inflict the maximum damage, petrol and gunpowder had been used, setting off a series of explosions which went on for hours. Everything was smouldering. The library of religious books written in different languages 600 years before the birth of Christ, the precious rugs and the holy altar were all turned to ash within hours. It appeared as if the serene, half-closed eyes of the Buddha were averting themselves from the sight of the havoc all around. The burnt ruins of the monasteries seemed to belong to an older, more primitive time, questioning the very notion of modern civilisation. The bare and wrecked shrines and the disfigured Buddha looked helpless and naked under the sky. The violence and atrocity stunned the Bodhisattvas and future Buddhas. Constellations thousands of light-years away witnessed the devastation.

Anil and Sunil were on their beds when their houses were set on fire, barely managing to escape from their houses in time. The villagers tried to pour water on the fire but could not stop it from spreading. They were gazing from a distance after several attempts to put out the unstoppable fire. Everyone was crying and screaming for help. The mob was looting and ransacking. The victims fled to the forest to save their lives. The fire ripped through the villages and left smoky, charred and smouldering ruins.

The next morning Anil and Sunil returned to the place where their houses should had been, but no recognisable trace remained. Burnt walls and gates stared at them. Together they were running a shop, near the monasteries which had been looted.

Anil asked: "When did you see the fire?"

"I was in bed," Sunil replied. "The brightness of the sky woke me up. The flames lit up the whole area."

Anil asked with despair and anger: "Who would do this? How dare they?"

Sunil replied: "I heard it was that Facebook image which provoked it."

"A photograph! It's unacceptable," Anil shook his head. "Mindless vandalism."

Sunil hushed him. "Be careful what you are saying, the walls have ears."

But there were no walls. Everything was burnt, and the ashes had blown away.

Government officials, police officers and local political leaders all arrived in the morning. The head monk was so devastated that he couldn't speak.

One senior monk mourned: "I have never seen this type of barbarism in my lifetime. I sheltered the Muslim community during the 1971 Liberation War. I hid them behind the shrine of this very Buddha to protect them from the Pakistani Army. So what, after 40 years, makes them suddenly want to demolish us? Facebook, Twitter, WhatsApp – all these modern technologies should be banned if they cause hatred and crime."

The official in charge said: "We are sorry to see the damage. We will find the perpetrators."

The head monk said: "This statue of Buddha was 300 years old".

"We will recommend that the central government helps you build a new monastery."

"How do we replace the Buddha's relics or ancient manuscripts? Do you think 300 year-old statues grow on trees?"

In three days' time, all the top brass and their underlings visited the smoking remains. The Prime Minister travelled from Dhaka by helicopter to view the wreckage, sanctioning 140 million taka (around £1.2m) to build new monasteries.

The following week, the head monk delivered a sermon under the open sky. The enlightened world was listening to him.

Afterwards, Anil said: "Honourable Monk, you did not protest strongly enough."

"We are human beings, Anil. When dogs bite us, we do not bite them back."

Sunil said: "They destroyed our homes and heritage. You are asking us to be silent?"

Anil added: "They will mistake our politeness for weakness."

The head monk replied with a deep sigh: "Do you know how many monasteries have been burned in previous centuries? From Afghanistan to Indonesia, thousands of monasteries were attacked and demolished. This is nothing. Evil people may burn the monastery to the ground, shatter our statues and ransack the shrine, but they cannot annihilate two and a half thousand years of Buddhist teaching."

The attack on the monasteries dented the secular façade of Bangladesh. The Prime Minister pleaded for sustained harmony between the religions in the country and called for appropriate punishment for the perpetrators. Restoration and rebuilding were watched over by the Bangladesh military and border guards, as a never-ending stream of political leaders and high officials made their journey to exhibit solidarity and support for the Buddhists.

Newly-built monasteries with modern facilities and landscaped parks draw tourists from all over the country. The thatched monastery roof was replaced with concrete tiles. Now that everyone can access them, the former serenity and tranquillity of the monasteries has given way to chaos: the devotees are replaced by selfie-mad tourists who nevertheless provide a new source of income for the monasteries.

Anil and Sunil were chatting before closing their shop for the day.

Anil said: "So many tourists have been coming since the restoration! Profits are up."

Sunil replied: "My mother says she can't meditate with all the noise."

Anil emphasised: "The senior monk was also complaining about the crowds. You just can't please the older generation! Your mother should not go to the temple to meditate and the senior monk could always just lead meditation in the forest instead."

Sunil expressed his concern: "What on earth's the point of having a monastery if it isn't used for religious services?"

Anil answered: "Be practical, don't be silly and be grateful for all the material benefits. Have you finished counting the takings?"

However, it was far more difficult to rebuild the trust between the two communities. The broken neck of the statue of the Buddha can be repaired and restored with paint and plaster, but the cleverest plastic surgeon would be challenged to conceal the scars in modern civilisation.

A Country Run by Allah

We were returning from the capital city, Dhaka, to our hometown of Chittagong. We were four passengers in the car. It was a Toyota Starlet 5-door hatchback, a durable, compact car which served its purpose on our bumpy roads. It had been reconditioned in Japan for sale in Bangladesh. My father and the driver were in the front seats and my sister, my mother and I in the back seat.

It had been pouring with rain for several days. Our monsoons always last for two or three weeks without a break. The highways were wet and surface water covered most of the roads. We were fortunate that the motorways were not yet inundated by water because they were higher than the surrounding land. All the ditches and fields were flooded. "Water, water, water, everywhere nor any drop to drink," recited my poetry-loving mother.

In those days, the Dhaka to Chittagong highway was just a single carriageway without a central reservation island. Long-distance coaches, trucks and heavy goods vehicles thundered along. The buses were constantly pulling out to overtake in the most dangerous spots. Hand carts and pedal-powered vehicles, like rickshaws and tuk-tuk vans all shared the same road with the motorised vehicles. Even cattle and dogs were on the roads, especially near the bazaars. The traffic was utterly chaotic.

The air conditioning in the car was not working so we had to keep the windows open in order to bear the suffocating heat. The gentle breeze kept us cool despite the high humidity, but the splashing of the surface water and gusting rain forced us to close the windows several times.

The distance from Dhaka to Chittagong is one hundred and thirty miles. On a good day, it took six to seven hours to travel between those two cities. On that particular day, the traffic was not heavy. We passed smoothly through Jatrabari, Daudkandi and Chandina and reached Comilla in three hours. Comilla was half way between Dhaka and Chittagong and famous for its special sweets called Rashamalai which were sold in several service stations and restaurants. We took a break and had our lunch. My father bought two kilograms of best Rashamalai from a famous shop and we set off. It was half past three: we had about four more hours' journey ahead.

I was reading a novel. My mother and sister were dozing beside me as we drove. Suddenly I saw a truck run in front of us. There was a cracking noise. Our car spun 180 degrees, hit a roadside tree and fell into a ditch. It landed on its roof.

It took a couple of minutes to understand what had happened. Three of the windows were closed, but fortunately one window had been open when we crashed, so we climbed out through it. I still remember my father was quite fat, we didn't know how he managed to squeeze through such a small space. The windscreen was shattered and my father suffered cuts to his right hand from the broken glass but unbelievably none of us had any injuries apart from the laceration of my father's hand. My thick novel and the packets of Rashamalai were floating in the ditch. I wished I could grab the book before it sank. The driver hurried to get the essential documents from the glove compartment of the crashed car. It looked like a scene from a Hollywood film.

We all were shaken and thanking Allah that we were safe. A lot of people gathered to watch the accident. Everyone was shouting and looking at us but nobody offered a helping hand. They had simply come to look at the circus that we provided when we were desperately climbing out the car. Smart phones and Facebook were not available in those days. Otherwise I'm sure the pictures would have gone viral. The crowd usually gathered after an accident to shout advice but not to help. People were coming in waves from nearby villages and they were clearly disappointed that there were no casualties and that they could not loot anything from the car and the scene.

My father asked our driver to go to the nearby garage and find a recovery vehicle while we had to stay there to look after our car. As usual, the truck driver had fled from the scene and no one helped but shouted and gesticulated instead. There was neither an ambulance nor a police car to be seen and there would have been more hope of finding rescuers on Mars. The rescuers could be seen in Chicago Hope or Gray's Anatomy, not on the streets of Bangladesh.

After an hour, two men arrived on a motorbike. One of them looked like a political leader from the village. He was chewing betel nuts and spitting mouthfuls of betel-nut juice everywhere. He introduced himself as Sagir.

He said: "Hello, is everyone okay, why are you waiting here?"

My father answered: "Our driver's gone to the garage, looking for help to get the car out of the ditch."

"What a cock and bull story! It's obvious you were drunk and driving, and you're spinning a yarn to escape justice."

My father held onto his temper, knowing there was no point in arguing. Patiently, we fetched the car's blue book and our driver's licence. My father had never learned to drive a car. Eventually Sagir and his friend left, having found no way of extorting money from us.

About forty minutes later, a police van was passing. The officer stopped, sorry to see us standing in the rain. He asked us to follow him to the nearby police station, thirty minutes' walk away, where we could shelter. The station turned out to be a shed with a table and one chair, which was offered to my mother. My sister and I stood in the shed, my sister shivering with cold and the trauma. We left my father standing by the car.

It was another hour before my father came to collect us in the recovery vehicle, towing our wrecked Toyota. We reached Chittagong at midnight and we all thanked Allah.

Bangladesh must be one of the countries run by Allah. He is omnipresent and saves us. No human authorities would be able to tackle the chaotic traffic there. The country and its people could not survive natural calamities or man-made disasters without an Allah.

A Driving Lesson

Before starting at university I had a month to spare so I decided to have some driving lessons. I approached my mother as she was always very keen to satisfy my whims. She asked one of my uncles to give me lessons. In a few days' time my uncle phoned and agreed to our request.

He was my first driving instructor. Although he himself did not have any experience in giving driving tuition, he had been driving for thirty years and owned a garage. He was middle-aged, comparatively tall and heavily-built. He had an aristocratic moustache, a head full of hair, and was the sort of the person who does not care what the world thinks about him.

My first lessons took place very early in the morning. Although the roads were comparatively empty, my uncle did not want to take any risks on the road, so we used to go a nearby field for moving-off drill. It took me quite a while to find the biting point of the clutch: the engine would growl for ages. The most fundamental of driving skills, learning to change gear, was really hard for the first couple of lessons. I began to get the hang of the six-point check (left blind spot, left wing mirror, rear-view mirror, front of the car, right wing mirror and right blind spot) and the emergency stop. All were practised in the field.

In a week's time I was gaining confidence with starting, pulling away from the kerb and moving forward. Mirror, signal and manoeuvre were mastered as well. I was very proud of myself, I started day-dreaming about driving to university and surprising everyone in the class with my skill, especially those smart boys who looked down on girls.

By the tenth or twelfth lesson, I could not exactly recall, my uncle was feeling sufficiently confident with my performance and asked me to drive back home from the field where we practised. I was excited and pleased to be driving on the street. It was about half-past seven in the morning. There were very few vehicles in the street. I was driving very carefully. In those days, there were not many female drivers on the road so the pedestrians were just staring at me and passing comments. As the windows were open and the speed was low, I could hear them yelling at me, "Look, look, a lady driver, nothing to do in life, just enjoying herself." I wasn't particularly worried, as I knew my uncle was very protective and could be very vocal if necessary. Moreover, he'd drilled me not to be distracted by anything while driving.

At the next turning, a rickshaw pulled out from the slip road in front of me. I saw it but couldn't stop quickly enough: I lost control of the car. I felt my car crash into the rickshaw, throwing the driver to the ground. Fortunately, he had no passengers in the vehicle. My uncle pulled the handbrake, bringing the car to a stop. The rickshaw was a complete wreck. The wheels of the rickshaw were completely broken.

A lot of people gathered in the street as usual to get a glimpse of me, the circus clown. Everyone was shouting and one mam cried: "Look, it was that girl caused it! Women are at the root of all this world's disasters. Safer for everyone if they are kept out of the drivers' seat."

My uncle was bold and kept his nerve. He jumped out of the car and looked at the crowd and shouted, "Stop all this nonsense, what is the problem?"

The rickshawala was standing on the pavement and trembling at the sight of his vehicle. He was a middle-aged, small-built, stick-thin person, wearing a faded shirt and a dirty lungi, with a small piece of cloth hanging around his neck to wipe away his sweat. His cheekbones were prominent beneath the hollows of his eyes and his collarbones protruded though his faded shirt. His face was unshaven and his hair was uncombed.

Calling him over, my uncle offered him some cash. The rickshawala started arguing about the money and complaining that it would not be sufficient to repair the damaged wheels. My uncle angrily replied in his loudest voice, "You should be grateful that we stopped and paid you compensation. We could have just driven off without stopping." We quickly changed places in the driving seat and left the spot immediately.

By this stage I was trembling and sweating with fear and adrenaline, and nearly broke down in tears. Seeing me struggling to control my emotions, my uncle – who'd not said a harsh word about the crash – rebuked me for weakness. He told me to be brave in this type of situation and we returned home safely. My uncle explained the accident to my parents in detail. He was not in the least scared, telling my father that he had come across this type of incident several times during his life. The important thing was to keep calm and tackle the situation diplomatically. Having heard all the details, my father ordered me to cease my driving lessons. He blamed my tender age for the accident. My lessons stopped there and then. That was the end of my driving lessons in Bangladesh.

Now I cannot help thinking, if there'd been a fatality, would my uncle have stopped and got out of the car to give compensation? And if so, what would he have thought was a fair price? Or would he just have fled the spot?

Our Music Tutor

Our music tutor was called Ostad Promotha Sinha. The title "Ostad" denotes a distinguished musical scholar and performer. He first visited our house with a flautist friend of our family. Ostad Promotha Sinha was fat and short. His protruding tummy and long curly hair made him unattractive. His voice was very deep. He was chewing betel nuts throughout the time he stayed in our house and spitting red betel juice into the ashtray. He was appointed as our tutor due to his reputation as a renowned vocalist although I had never heard that my bookish parents listened to his performances on radio or television.

He asked our parents to buy a set of tabla and a tanpura. The tabla are percussion instruments consisting of a pair of hand drums. It is not easy to play the tabla and requires strong actions of the fingers and palms to produce different sounds and rhythms. It usually works as an accompaniment for voices or other instruments. It is mostly played by men as it requires strong hands to create the rhythm. My parents did not have any background knowledge of music and were not keen to buy a tabla as we two sisters were to be the students. Somehow Ostad convinced us that we don't need to play the tabla, as he himself would play them to accompany us, but without them the classical music would not be complete. The tanpura is a supporting instrument for sustaining the melody of the vocalist. It is a long-necked stringed instrument that produces a continuous harmonic bourdon. It is not difficult to play and has four strings and a large base. The combined sounds of all the strings merge with the tone of the vocalist. In addition, Ostad advised us to upgrade our old harmonium, a keyboard instrument which produces sound by blowing air through its reeds. As instructed, my generous and over-excited parents bought the tabla, tanpura and upgraded the harmonium so that all the accompanying instruments were new, fresh and ready to make music.

However, we two vocalists were not new, fresh and ready to make music. Firstly, we didn't like the Ostad, but more importantly we didn't enjoy playing the harmonium and we were not good vocalists either, although we'd both attended music school. To be honest, our singing was extremely poor but we carried on with it as a hobby because going to music school was so much fun. We liked playing in the park on the way and picking flowers from the woodlands. Now that the interesting element of the music lessons had been eliminated, only the boring stuff remained.

Vocalists need to practise, practise and practise. Some skill in melody and rhythm, and inner motivation are also required. Every aspect of musicality was lacking in both of us. Parental ambition alone cannot create good singers but my parents did not give up. They tried in vain to train our ears, playing us the finest tunes. We could perhaps have become musicologists in time but never performers. Musicologist is a scholar who studies music as an academic subject, as opposed to a performer or a composer.

Soon the day arrived for the first lesson with our new teacher. My parents were relieved that we didn't need to take a long walk and waste our valuable time on the journey to our music lessons. We usually call male tutors "Sir" and female tutors "Apa or Didimoni" but on the first day Ostad instructed us that he was to be addressed as 'Ostadji' and that we were to show him reverence by touching his feet. All the instruments should be respected in the similar way, by touching them. He reminded us of the Goddess of knowledge, Saraswathi, who carries in her hands a musical instrument, books and everything related to knowledge.

In a typical one-hour lesson, most of the time was spent in tuning the tabla and tanpura, and the rest in teaching. Ostad would write out musical notes in his artistic handwriting. He gave lessons only in classical music, 'the mother of all music', on which he told us we should build the pillars of our musicality. So our day-dreams of singing modern songs in the chorus for the school cultural programme were nipped in the bud. We could see that 'Sa, Re, Ga Ma, Pa, Dha, Ni, Sa' ('Do, Re, Mi, Fa, Sol, La, Ti, Do') was not going to work for us. It was the most boring thing that could happen to nine and ten-year old girls. We were ordered to do vocal exercises every single day for an hour. The neighbours mocked our screeches as, at the close of every school-day, we obediently remained inside to practise while all the other children played. It was torture.

One of our relatives heard that my parents had appointed Ostad as our music tutor. She warned my mother that his character was not good as he drank alcohol and had been dismissed from school due to his addiction. Nevertheless, my parents remained adamant. Although alcohol was prohibited in our house, my father only said: "Performers need to drink alcohol to relieve stress on the stage. Our community does not know how to value a talent." My mother decided to guard us and used to sew clothes during the lessons.

They say 'practice makes perfect', but no amount of hard work will turn crows into canaries. My sister and I seemed to actually get worse over time. We were growing in size but due to lack of interest and practice, our voices were deteriorating. Certainly the tutor came and went without any discernible improvement in our performance.

One winter night our teacher was found drunk and unconscious in the street. He was taken to hospital and treated with first aid. My father received the news gravely but still Ostad did not lose his job although my mother did order that he should not be allowed to teach us unless another adult was at home. This was our chance for some fun – and so, whenever our parents were out, we shouted through the veranda that the doors were locked, giggling as the protruding tummy and long curly hair executed a U-turn.

As we progressed to senior school, there was no longer time to allow us music lessons. Our parents wanted us to concentrate more on studying and preparing for our O-levels. At last, Ostad was asked to leave, not because of his addiction but because our priorities had changed.

It was only a couple of years later that we read in the newspaper that 'the renowned singer, Ostad Promotha Sinha' had been admitted to hospital and died. It was rumoured that he suffered from cirrhosis of the liver due to chronic alcoholism. My father was distraught that Ostad's drinking had destroyed his talent. The few tributes that were paid to him in no way reflected the scale of his musical accomplishments.

The Migrant Worker

Although I had graduated from university I couldn't find a job and my life of unemployment was very depressing and frustrating. My unproductive days started very early in the morning and finished late at night. I commuted to the nearest city to hunt for a job.

I'd applied for every vacancy advertised in the newspapers over the last two years and managed to secure a couple of interviews but was never offered a position. I wondered if it was the lack of influential contacts that held me back, or my unfashionable clothes and outdated get up.

My father always berated me for my worthless life. The other boys from our village, who didn't have degrees, left the country for the Middle East. One of them was called Mustak. On a recent visit to our house he had come loaded with perfumes, cigarettes and sweets, to brag and swank like a big man. His family invited the whole community to a get-together, celebrating his success. My father was very keen to have a word with him and his parents and get their advice about my following his footsteps and going to work in the Middle East. Mustak's parents suggested my family pay a broker to arrange everything, from my air tickets and accommodation, to securing me a job.

My father was very pleased with the plan. Before I knew it, we were deep in negotiations, the only problem being the size of the broker's fee. To raise the sum demanded for his services, my father was contemplating selling all the land that he farmed. Undaunted, I reassured him that all the foreign currency I would earn would soon buy him double what he'd sacrificed.

Having decided to sell the land however, another problem arose: the farm had been inherited from my grandfather, the land should have been divided at his death between my father and his six brothers, but no formal arrangement had ever been made regarding the boundaries of their individual shares. To sell the amount of land we wanted to, we'd need all my uncles to agree to our plan but every single one of them refused. One even advised my father not to send me to the Middle East at all, recounting a story he'd heard about a client who'd been cheated by his broker and given fake documents. The man had been forced to return on the next available flight and had lost everything. My uncle went so far as to help me to find funding to start a business in Bangladesh, but to my father and me it only seemed like an attempt to destroy our dreams. The two brothers fell out.

In great despair, my father sold his own portion of the land but the amount he raised came to only half the amount demanded by the broker, forcing him to borrow from his friends. Seeing our disappointment, my mother handed over her gold jewellery, all the ornaments that traditionally should have been kept for my future bride. Still adamant to leave for the Middle East, I didn't care and promised to buy new, modern jewellery on my return.

On the night of my departure I was very excited. All my extended family came to see me off at the airport. I was moved to see the tears streaming down my father's cheeks and wished I could have secured a job at home in Bangladesh. I felt suddenly sad to be leaving my beloved family and I went through passport control in great distress. But on meeting a couple of boys from my own village in the queues, my confidence returned at the sight of familiar faces. Soon I was boarding an aeroplane for the first time and was amazed to find the flight was jam-packed with labourers.

We arrived at Dubai in four hours. Dubai International Airport was distinctly busy and seemed gigantic in comparison to the airport I'd just left. This one looked as though it could have easily held a couple of football stadiums with room left over. Thousands of passengers were hurrying about in the lobby and I thought I would get lost among such an ocean of people. The duty-free shops were mesmerising with their array of products and dazzling lights.

Passing to Dubai's passport control, I assisted a couple of fellow-passengers in filling out their embarkation cards. They certainly weren't going to get help from any of the officers there: although I had learned English at primary school and taken a crash course in English conversation, I could barely understand the immigration officers' questions. Their attitude and behaviour were disgraceful but, like a flock of sheep, we obediently complied with every order and command.

Everyone in the airport, from security guards to cleaners, was very hostile and made it their mission to harrass us whenever possible: the security man taunted us about our cheap baggage and clothes; the cleaners in front of the toilet jeered at us as one of our fellow passengers spilled water on the floor while making his ablutions for prayer. I actually spotted one of my old schoolmates working as a porter in the airport but he pretended not to recognise me and avoided catching my eye. I was shocked to hear the cleaners speaking in Bengali among themselves.

The broker had assured my parents that someone would be waiting at the arrival lounge to receive me and take me to my accommodation, but no one was there and nobody came, though I waited in the terminal for five hours. At last, a few of us hired a taxi to take us to the address the broker had given me.

The accommodation we'd arranged turned out to be in a dilapidated building. Our room had four beds. My bed needed to be shared with someone else. The good news was that my bedmate worked as a night watchman, so the arrangement was at least mutually very convenient: I slept at night while he was on duty and he used the bed while I was at work. The accommodation had one toilet and one kitchen for twenty of us.

Since I was an English-speaker with a university degree, the broker had assured us I was guaranteed a supervisor's post. The morning after our arrival, I was taken straight to the building site of a Formula 1 track. The person in charge, however, said I was to work as a bricklayer. I would have to lay bricks in the glaring sun every day from 6am to 8pm with only a one-hour break. I was my parents' youngest son and had never done a stroke of manual work all my life. If the temperature of our country hit the mid-thirties, I would simply refuse to leave the house. In the worst of the summer heat, my father would head into the fields to supervise the day labourers while I pampered myself with the electric fan. This officer was asking me to stay in the sun in the temperature of forty to forty-five degrees. I was absolutely horrified. The whole situation and arrangement had been based on lies. As it turned out, I wasn't even skilled enough to be a bricklayer. I would have to be the bricklayers' porter. The village boys who were sons of bricklayers were better placed to succeed out there than I, a graduate with no discernible practical abilities.

Remembering my uncle's grave warning about the broker, I hated myself for not taking his advice. I should have been trying to start a business! I wanted desperately to leave Dubai on the next flight home, but how? I had to pay my father's debt. I had also promised him to buy more land for cultivation, and that I'd buy new ornaments for my mother to give to my eventual bride.

How could I possibly earn that amount of money on my small wage? The salary I earned would provide me only with food. The so-called accommodation was free for only two days and then I would have to pay to rent the bed for twelve hours out of every twenty-four. I could barely save any money.

I am thirty years old. I'll have to save every penny for the next thirty years to gather enough money to fulfil my promises. I've decided never to tell my parents about my situation in Dubai. If I'm ever able to return to visit my parents again, I'll tell them I work as a supervisor: to admit I am working as an orderly would humiliate my whole family and everything they sacrificed to send me here. It has all been my fault: it was I who longed to work in the Middle East. It is impossible to struggle against my fate. I am trapped: I can only resign myself to my lot.

The Maidservant

Bakul came to our house when I was ten years old. She bore a physical resemblance to us as she was a distant cousin. She was fourteen years old and short in stature for her age with long, black hair. Her complexion was dark due to prolonged exposure to the sun. Her nose was flat and she wore a stud in her left nostril. Her imitation-gold earrings were cheap and had been bought at the village fair, a present from her elder brother. She came with only a half-empty polythene bag of belongings: some underwear, and coal for use as toothpaste; she'd been told that city dwellers did not have coal. She did not bring a comb or toothbrush. Bakul had only had one other frock which she had given to her sister as a present, knowing that we would give her new clothes.

Her parent's hut was next to my maternal grandparents' house. It had only one room and a veranda to house a family of nine. All the five sisters slept in that room, with the two boys occupying the veranda. The kitchen was a shed outside the hut. My grandparents' two-storey mansion soaked up the sun and tipped the rain over the roof of the hut. Bakul's father was a day labourer but unable to feed his family from his small income, so the daughters were sent to the city to work as helping hands while the boys were allowed to carry on their education.

Bakul looked after my younger sister and did the household chores while my mother taught at school. My little sister was only two years old, had just started to run and got up to mischief everywhere. Bakul liked to cuddle the little one all day as she took my sister for one of her own siblings. She had been going to her village primary school but could not continue her education beyond that, due to the family's poverty. However, she was far from illiterate. We used to play board games and map games together. A map game is finding a city, town or place on the map of Bangladesh. She was good at it. She knew all the major cities in Bangladesh and could easily find even very tiny places on the map like Kaliganj, Elliotganj, Shibganj or Hajiganj. She was a keen reader and devoured most of our story books. She liked to organise our bookshelves and could promptly find anything we were looking for. While we were learning how to do kitting and crochet she learned quickly before us by using our leftover yarns. When I won a scholarship in my fifth year, my father rewarded me with a big wall-clock. Bakul could soon understand the Roman numerals and announce the precise time. She became one of our family members. However, though human rights, female education and female empowerment are fine theories, they are not practised in our community. Nobody tried to continue her education, so after primary school it came to an end. The unwritten plan was that Bakul would stay with us as long as her family needed money or until her parents received a suitable marriage proposal. Her parents received five hundred taka per month for her to stay with us. My mother used to say we would give her a gold chain for her wedding. Everyone was very pleased with her work.

Four years after Bakul's arrival, her mother came to our house. My mother was uneasy as she sensed something sinister on the horizon, probably a marriage proposal. But Bakul had apparently received a better job offer. My mother angrily demanded who was willing to give more money and provide a guarantee of safety. The hesitant answer was that the offer was not from another household, but a garment factory. The clothing industry was taking its first steps in our economy, recruiting teenage girls with minimal education and skills to staff factories. A broker had offered two thousand taka per month. My mother tried to explain that Bakul would need food, accommodation and security, so she'd be lucky to have more than five hundred taka a month left over; instead she offered to increase Bakul's salary, even double it. But Bukul's mother told mine not to fret about the girl's safety because her elder brother, who could not finish high school, had a security post in the same factory. They would rent a room in the city and share the cost. Adamant, she took Bakul from our house.

Many years later now, we have all drifted away from the house. I settled in the UK. My mother retired and my father passed away, so my mother lives on her own there now. On my last trip home, my mother told me that Bakul had paid her a recent visit. Bakul was very apologetic for leaving to go to the factory. A few years ago, part of a sewing machine had dropped on her left leg, causing a complicated fracture of the tibia and the fibula. The factory did not provide any medical help and Bakul did not have enough money to pay for treatment. She neglected the injury and ultimately she developed gangrene, but survived the septic shock after having her leg amputated below the knee. Despite her disability she returned to the factory as soon as she could and continued to work. However, recently the factory had caught fire. Her brother, together with hundreds of other workers, died in the stampede. Bakul was only saved because she had taken the day off sick.

The factory has closed forever. Now, she is begging my mother to take her as a maidservant again, insisting that she could do all the household chores, even with only one leg. With no savings, she is in danger of dying of starvation. My mother gave her some cash but is unable to provide her with a job.

Now, when I go to *Marks & Spencer* and *Next* to buy clothes, I always check the label. When the tag says "Made in Bangladesh", I am instantly reminded of the many lost limbs, spirits and souls.

The Flight Attendant

When I was born, my parents were very pleased. Firstly, I was male, and gender was extremely important in our culture, and secondly, I had a pale complexion. Unlike our neighbour, who'd just been landed with a dark-skinned baby girl, my proud mother was delighted to have me with two accolades from Allah – not just a boy, but a peach-coloured little angel. In the communal play area, no one cuddled that dark girl; I was always adored and snuggled up. My mother said that my walking and running were delayed as a toddler because adults would continually carry me about and cosset me.

My childhood and youth were very exciting. I was always popular among my female classmates who made no secret of admiring my good looks. Everyone adored me because it was impossible not to be struck by my smart appearance. Secretly, I had a girlfriend: only average-looking but very intelligent. Her eyes were her best feature, with long, curved eyelashes, and I loved her long, black hair that would billow out like clouds. She would compose long poems for me, reciting them to me in her melodious voice. All her family were clever, both her parents were educated and worked in non-governmental organisations.

After obtaining my degree in geography, I secured a job at a village high school. As usual, all my students were attracted by my looks. I loved teaching: it was very exciting to show the students the political and geographical map of the world. I was mentally visiting its most beautiful places during my classes: on Monday, climbing Kilimanjaro; Tuesday, walking in Victoria Falls; on Wednesday, on safari in Kenya; Thursday, trekking around Machu Picchu; Friday I was roaming Patagonia and on Saturday strolling around the Louvre. In my daydreams, I was sunbathing in the Mediterranean Sea and diving in Sumatra. I tried to inspire the students to open their eyes and look for new adventures every day. It must be said, though, that despite the respect and high social standing I received as a teacher, my village school-teacher's salary was pretty poor. In our country, the teacher of a village school can't aspire to much beyond a lower middle-class life. Luxuries like taking holidays, foreign travel, even owning their own car and apartment, are out of reach.

Yet I yearned to travel the world. Combining my degree in geography with my thirst for travel, I secretly applied for a job as a steward in Emirates Airways. I sent in my application thinking that this would be the best way to see the world and get paid for it. Against my expectations, I found myself offered the job, probably because of my clean-cut appearance and education. I admired the glamorous outfit of the flight attendants. I fantasised about walking in the beautiful cities and the rare opportunities to experience the local life of different cultures. I would dream of spending nights in five star-hotels all over the world. When I confessed to my family, they were all enormously proud of my achievement: the wages of a steward would be more lucrative than my teaching' salary. And so, within a few weeks, I had resigned from the school and begun my new job.

In my epaulettes, white shirt and royal blue blazer I couldn't have felt smarter. We were trained on how to talk, walk, and carry ourselves and given lessons in trolley-pushing etiquette. To an outside observer, we looked like movie stars. Although there was not a huge difference between the basic salaries of the teachers and flight crews, when we add my flight time and layover allowances, it would be double the salary of a village school teacher. In a few years, I had bought an apartment and a car with my new-found wealth. My parents were even more delighted and the neighbours envied the steep rise of my earnings. I could not predict my forthcoming disappointment.

My girlfriend and I broke up, as her family rejected my marriage proposal. Her parents refused to hand over their daughter to an airline steward, unable to accept their future son-in-law carrying trays for the passengers. In their eyes there was no difference between my job and that of any street porter. My girlfriend hated that my profession involved spending nights in the air, preventing me attending Eid or other festivals with the family. She begged me to leave the job and lead a normal life again. I refused outright, telling her I'd found my dream job. It seemed to me that hers was not true affection, which appeared to be confirmed when I heard, only a couple of months later,that she'd got married to a nine-to-five civil servant. I hope she writes more poems for her beloved husband who will be awestruck by her talent.

I saw her one day not long ago in a shopping centre, dragging three poorly-dressed children along, her hair badly in need of a good trim. She cannot have enough money for any nice things in her life. Briefly, I wondered if I'd have been happier as a teacher and with her still. But, admiring my reflection in the duty-free shop window, I considered that regret was a luxury I could do without.

Now, my conscience sometimes troubles me. I miss being treated with the respect I enjoyed as a teacher, but my property and bank balance cushion me from the fire of my conscience with their comforting presence.

The Rickshawala

The rickshaw is the cheapest form of transport. The Chinese brought this pedalled vehicle to the Indian subcontinent. As a child, every time we left the house, we would see several rickshawalas. It is a widely-available and affordable means of making short journeys. We hire rickshaws to go anywhere, from the school run to shopping trips. It is the cheapest form of travel as it is pedalled by man power and incurs no running costs.

The rickshawalas are usually the village folk who cannot find work locally. They left their villages to escape unemployment and starvation and migrated to the big cities. The government is unable to provide work for these unskilled labourers but they easily learn how to pedal their vehicles, so huge working resources are wasted as they take up this trouble-free source of guaranteed income.

We lazy city-dwellers prefer a comfortable journey in a rickshaw to fighting our way along the street. With our pavements crowded with hawkers, walking is not an attractive option, even for short distances. Rickshaws can be safer too for women, who try to avoid walking alone or even using public transport because of the risk of sexual harassment and assault (euphemistically called Eve teasing) on their commute to work or school. Hiring a rickshaw has become a social norm and, if a lady walks in the street, she's judged as being too poor or too stingy to hire a rickshaw.

Several rickshawalas would sit at the entrance of girls' colleges or schools waiting for clients. The way they look at the girls is not always benign. One of my friends Sarah used to hate taking rickshaws, preferring to call a taxi which was expensive and not immediately available in front of the college gates. I refused to go with her by taxi as it cost four to five times more – at least, until she disclosed the following story to me.

She'd hired a rickshaw from college to her relative's house, a journey of nearly nine miles that usually took about forty-five minutes in light traffic. It was late afternoon, not very hot and not raining, with moderate humidity. The rickshawala was peddling at a high speed but kept glancing back at her.

Sarah shouted, "Look in front while you are driving! Why do you keep looking back?"

The rickshawala replied, "Don't worry, Apa (the typical title for young girls), I am an experienced driver. I have been working in Dhaka for the last five years. I could drive down this street blindfold."

"I don't care. I'm asking you to drive slowly and focus on the road."

The rickshawala persisted, "So Apa, you are a student, you read a lot? Are you going to take a job in an office? Which office will you choose?"

"I don't know! Would you please focus on your driving? Didn't you see that car moving away so quickly? You should be driving on the side of the road, not down the middle."

The rickshawala still went on, "I could not continue beyond primary school. I had to leave the village to find a job in the city."

Sarah was getting annoyed; we all know the history of the rickshawalas. This is the way they try to gain our sympathy. She pretended not to hear.

The rickshawala tried a different tack, "Where is your home district, Apa?"

Feeling it would be rude not to answer, Sarah replied, "Barishal."

"I am too! I would like to take you to my place."

That statement did not sound good to Sarah and she immediately suspected his motives. Straight away, the rickshawala picked up speed and overtook the other vehicles. He reached to stroke Sarah's left calf. It was now or never: Sarah jumped.

She landed heavily in the road, the contents of her satchel spilling across the street as the rickshawala pedalled away. She lay dazed and bruised, the glass of her wristwatch shattered. A passing man who'd seen her fall came hurrying to help her up. He asked how she had managed to tumble out of the rickshaw, but she didn't know what to say. He asked again: why was she alone? Why had she jumped? She did not tell him the rickshawala had assaulted her.

Sarah was ashamed to tell this incident to anyone and did not come forward to disclose this to the police. I was the first person to whom she'd ever told the story. Although the government has implemented the law to prevent Eve teasing, it is still happening in broad daylight due to our social stigma.

Ever since that experience, Sarah has hated riding in rickshaws. Hearing her story, I couldn't help think that the inconspicuousness and ubiquity of rickshaws gives any unscrupulous drivers a perfect cover to attack, in a city where we are at risk if we do, and at risk if we don't, allow them take us for a ride. This benign-looking yokel can be dangerous at any time if he gets the opportunity, and that it's precisely because of his sheer anonymity that women and girls will continue to fall prey to his greed and impropriety.

Ruined Future

Akbar was one of my uncle's six sons. We used to jokingly address him as Akbar the great. In reality, though, he was just a regular guy: not particularly talented, not particularly good-looking; really nice, but pretty much average in every way.

All the cousins of the family used to play together, sometimes painting or sometimes going off for the day to fish in the nearby canal. We always had the best times. One day Akbar came to our house with a huge box full of sweets as he had passed the higher secondary examination with good marks. He was very excited and looked smart in his new jeans and colourful shirt. My uncle and his family were very pleased with his performance in the examination. Three months later, he was admitted to university. We were all very proud of him.

He'd been given a place in the Department of Forestry Studies. Whenever we met up with him, he always liked to tell us every minute detail of university life – and we were desperately eager to know what everything was like. We'd quiz him for hours about the journey to university, the classrooms, the lecture galleries and even the girls in his class.

In his first year, his subjects were forest management, woodland ecology and conservation. He had to study trees, animal life and ecology. He was passionate and very connected with Nature. Even as children, Akbar's enjoyment and connection with nature had touched us. He used to visit the forest for fieldwork and had access to a large restricted area of woodland. He'd always called us cheeky monkeys and now described to us the vital importance of the monkeys' habitat for the ecology of the woodland. We used to hope he'd eventually get a job in Sundarban, the huge mangrove forest, and work as a forest ranger there. We always loved visiting the mangroves to see the Royal Bengal Tigers and the crocodiles in Sundarban. We used to joke that Akbar the Great would conquer all the wild animals. If everything went to plan, Akbar would be crowned King of the Forest, like a real-life Tarzan.

However, after a year of studies Akbar came to our house to say farewell. We were utterly amazed. He told us that he was abandoning his studies because he had been offered an opportunity to go to Hong Kong to work. My uncle had managed to save enough money to cover an agency fee, which meant he could send him abroad. My father was furious and could not tolerate this kind of short-sightedness from my uncle, striving to get Akbar to university only to have him quit a third of the way in.

My uncle tried to justify his decision by explaining that a university degree would not enable his son to earn as much money he could get in Hong Kong. Moreover, we did not have any high connections to pull strings and smooth the way for us, so in reality Akbar stood very little chance of securing a job as a Forest Officer, even after graduating.

Akbar would end up as another unemployed graduate lying around my uncle's house, like all his other brothers. He should therefore go to Hong Kong where he could earn some hard currency as some of the other boys in our village were doing. My father didn't speak with my uncle for a long time after this decision.

Akbar left the university and the country. He was only working as an unskilled labourer but his hard-earned foreign currency was worth several times its value when it reached our country. Akbar's wages soon enabled my uncle to build a five-storey mansion in the village. The status of my uncle was enhanced as he only had a corrugated tin-shed house before.

When he returned for a holiday, Akbar would once again come and visit us, just as before. Now we listened to stories about his life in Hong Kong. He was a good storyteller and we were eager listeners. We loved to hear about the culture and the food of Hong Kong, so different from Bangladesh, and all described by Akbar in minute detail. He brought packets of fried scorpions and crickets as delicacies.

After five years, Akbar had reached the limit of his visa: unable to extend it further, he had to leave Hong Kong. Returning to his village he found no savings left after five whole years of work, as my uncle's mansion had gobbled up all the money, leaving nothing for Akbar. He did not have any funding to start a business. With no degree and having worked abroad as a cheap labourer he had no skills or qualifications to apply for a job in our country.

He was unemployed for a long time before he finally managed to secure a clerking job in Sundarban, thanks to one of his old university friends who was working as a forest officer. He couldn't afford to travel over to visit us and we were not invited to visit him in Sundarban due to his severely reduced circumstances. Imagining how different things might have been for Akbar the Great, King of the Jungle, it was hard not to blame my uncle for his selfish avarice and short-sightedness.

Female Accommodation

Our student hostel was not big, but it was made up of two buildings. One was older, a three-storey block constructed sometime in the mid-1960s, while the newer one had been put up in the 1980s.

On my first day, the hostel superintendent, Dr Nushrat, ushered me into a big room on the second floor of the old building. I'd come with my father, travelling from our home in a different city. As it was female-only accommodation, my father had not been allowed beyond the visiting room, so I followed Dr Nushrat into the old building alone. The room was a dormitory, twenty metres wide and sixteen metres long, housing a row of five beds lined up next to each other.

I was the first to arrive, so the room was bare of any personal touch. I headed straight for the bed nearest the window, and loaded it with my mattress and pillow, piling alongside it my big trunk and hand luggage. The big trunk was to be used as a safe for storing cash and valuables. The beds were the usual hospital beds, steel-framed with a tall headboard. Each bed had, alongside it, a reading-table and wooden chair provided by the hostel.

Dr Nushrat informed me that in this five-bed dormitory she would actually have to accommodate twelve girls. I'd come to university in a cohort of female students who had all seized the opportunity to go to medical college, arriving together in a sudden influx. Previously, thirty per cent of the student population had been female, but in our year this figure rose to fifty percent. Dr Nushrat was puzzled and stressed by the challenge of allocating accommodation to so many more girls. I could not understand how twelve people were ever going to be able to sleep in the same room, let alone study. However, my father told me that the study of medical science could be done anywhere; in the dissection hall, the laboratory, tutorial rooms, the college library or even in the canteen.

Dr Nushrat told me that another girl had actually been allocated my bed. She reassured me that most of the girls had relatives in Dhaka, so that they would be using the room only during their leisure periods and wouldn't be staying overnight. My mental arithmetic was still struggling, however, to calculate how twelve pupils could be accommodated in five single beds, even when I was told that two girls were from Dhaka and would not be coming that night. That still left ten students to share the room: we would have to sleep together in pairs, head-to-tail. I pictured us all lying straight and stiff, like tinned sardines, not moving a limb all night: an extremely uncomfortable arrangement.

The hostel superintendent reassured me that this arrangement would only be necessary for a few weeks, and that within a month or two we would be allocated new rooms. In the end, however, we would remain in that room sharing beds for more than a year.

That first day, after arranging my bag and bedding, I went to say goodbye to my father. Seeing my expression, he told me not to worry, I would be so busy with my studies I wouldn't have time to be homesick. He gave me some cash for food: we wouldn't need travel expenses as the medical college was directly opposite the hostel. It seemed to me that he was leaving me in prison: inside I was crying desperately but I couldn't let him know. Together we walked to the gate. The taxi came and took him away to the train station to return to Chittagong. I was left alone at the hostel gate, tears flowing down my cheeks as the taxi disappeared from view. I was desperately tempted to hire a taxi with the money he'd given me for food, and follow him immediately back to the train station, but I didn't dare.

As well as the dormitory, our student hostel contained a common room which had a colour television with a satellite dish which enabled us to access more channels. At home, we were allowed to watch Bangladesh Television, CNN and BBC for educational purposes, but secretly we'd watched MTV or the late-night shows such as Dallas or Baywatch. Now I could watch whatever I wanted, but the remote control was always in the hands of the senior students. All the benches were arranged in rows and the senior students occupied the front row. Wherever I sat, I could barely ever see the TV screen, usually craning my head at an angle to catch a glimpse. The wooden benches were the most uncomfortable seats one could ever imagine: I missed our comfortable sofa at home. I felt more homesick in the TV room than anywhere else and rarely enjoyed anything I watched there.

The Students' Union kept a variety of newspapers in the common room, keeping them pinned to a standing table, so we had to read standing, leaning over the table. At home, I'd always used to take newspapers to bed and read in comfort before taking my afternoon nap. This new situation discouraged me from reading the paper, so my father advised me to keep one in my room to remain up to date with current affairs. The paperboy always left my paper just outside the door of our room which could have resulted in ten people wrestling over one newspaper. However, because my choice, '*The Bangladesh Observer*', was not popular among the students, I was saved a fight as it was an English newspaper and not easy to assimilate. The paper was always left intact for me, even though I never managed to open it on exam days.

We had to buy a bucket and mug for the showers as most of them never worked, though the taps were still functional. We had to save water in the bucket as water shortages were most frequent during the summer. The shower rooms were always busy and had queues in the afternoon although there were ten toilets and ten showers on every floor. As usual, the senior students took priority in the queues.

I had my breakfast, lunch, snacks and dinner in the canteen. I liked to have 'paratha' in the mornings, something my mother forbade me to eat daily at home because it was not healthy and I should avoid greasy food. Now I could have it for breakfast every single day. In the canteen, a serving of rice was presented in such a way that every grain was spread out on the surface making it look like a plateful. The dhal was only water stained with turmeric. The pieces of meat and fish were so thin that we thought they must be precision-cut to laboratory standards using a microtome. The cheapest meat was beef but one of my aunties had advised me against eating it. Some of my friends were very fussy about meat; they refused to use any spoon which had touched beef. Although I never ate it myself, I didn't care as much as that.

No male was allowed in our hostel except the paperboy and the guards. Male guardians or friends had to take a seat in the visiting room and a guard would shout up to our room to tell us there was a visitor. One day, a male student entered the hostel. One of my friends saw him in the corridor and she had a fit. The whole place erupted in chaos but as the male intruder was a political leader in our college, no action was taken. I never told the incident to my parents as they always believed that we were in the safest place in Dhaka and I didn't want to worry them.

We had a couple of flowering trees on the premises, a krishnachura and kodom tree, though the front and back gardens there were not big. We didn't have much recreation except the television and listening to music on a tape recorder. We used to walk on the rooftop just before sunset and enjoyed singing or gossiping. A few of my friends had very melodious voices and we used to sing along with Tagore, Manna Dey, Hemanta, Nachiketa. But Nachiketa was our favourite:

Sokatore oi kadiche sokole (Dear Lord, can you hear everyone crying?)

Coffee House er Sei addata aj ar nei (The chatter in the coffee house has silenced, we miss those golden days)

Tumi ki amai valobasho, (Do you love me? If you don't, I don't care. I get love and colour from the sun, I don't care about your gaudy love)

Jakhon somoy thamke darai (When time stands by, misfortune spreads its wings, our minds look for a quiet space, we dream for better days)

I used to recite poems from Tagore, Sunil or Rafiq Azad. One of my friends was so annoyed by my incessant recitation that she once tipped a full jug of water over my head to stop me.

Very occasionally we would walk to the Shaheed Meenar, the 'Language Martyrs Monument' or to the Bangladesh University of Engineering and Technology. Neither was more than a stone's throw from our hostel, but we almost never went. Newmarket, Nilkhet or Guasia were the nearest shopping centres, and always popular among students. For me, these expeditions were all efforts to fend off my homesickness, but I continued to suffer terribly; missing my parents, my city, my school friends, my house, my extended family and sometimes even the street lights of Chittagong.

One of my classmates brought a fridge into her room and put a notice board in front of it saying NO VACANCIES, meaning that no one was allowed to keep any food or drinks in her fridge, and no one could ask for cold water or ice, especially during the heat of summer. My father never indulged me with such a luxury although we could have afforded it. He would say "You need to learn to deal with hardships in life. It will help you become a better person."

At the weekend, most of the students would leave the hostel for their relatives' houses or the nearby city. Those whose homes were further away were the unfortunates, stuck in our accommodation, but we did have lots of fun cooking together, sitting, eating, drinking bottles of Coke. We would lie about on the floor, singing and giggling madly about nothing. One of our seniors used to say "Only you lot could seem drunk after just Coca-Cola and chicken biryani."

I enjoyed the new freedom to visit museums or attend live concerts while staying in the hostel but I never crossed boundaries and always returned by 7pm. Any student who returned after ten at night would be summoned to the superintendent to receive a telling-off.

In the medical college we had our own student library and study room. We were all allowed to use it, but the seats were usually occupied by senior boys or couples. It was considered suspicious behaviour if a female student went alone, no matter how much she explained she was only going to work. We did not want to be stigmatised and accused of having boyfriends by studying in the library.

My parents had given me a phone card and I tried my best to keep it for as long as possible. When returning to the hostel after a visit home, I would call my parents, but would limit myself to: "Arrived safely."

My friend teased, "You've invented the art of the telephone-telegram. Two seconds!"

Living in the UK now, I am struck by the luxury and comfort of student life. Every doctor all over the world obtains the same qualifications, covering the same syllabus, studying the same human anatomy, physiology and pathology, but the student atmosphere is completely different here. Strangely, though I moved so much further away, I did not suffer much homesickness after leaving Bangladesh because I had got over it while staying in the hostel. Life in the hostel was never glamorous, but I learned a lot. I am daily thankful and grateful for the self-reliance and strength it developed in me. I believe everyone needs to live for some time independently in order to grow up and become their true self.

Counterproductive

Our classmate, Shabnam, was her parent's only daughter. She was smart, hard-working and one of the brightest students in our class. Her complexion was not fair, but she had lovely eyes. She was a shy girl, uninterested in making conversation unless it was about our studies. The teachers appreciated her homework and were impressed by her good behaviour in class. While some of us got caught up debating the merits of gripping short stories – Chekhov's "The Kiss" or de Maupassant's "The Necklace" – Shabnam would be busily revising algebraic formulae.

One Parents' Day, my mother bumped into Shabnam's father. We were doing A-levels at that time, both combining physics, chemistry and mathematics, which required us to maintain a high standard of work at a very high level of difficulty.

Shabnam's father spent ages probing my mother about my general performance and what revision timetable I followed during the holidays. Although generally my mother hovered around me so much that I called her a helicopter mother, she never intervened in my studies. She would nag me to finish school projects on time and always chauffeured me to my lessons, but she'd not been a science student and had little understanding of higher mathematics or physics. It would have been impossible for her to help me interpret Boyle's law or the third equation of Newton.

Shabnam's father informed my mother that he had read and revised the whole science syllabus to support Shabnam. He also composed a revision file for his daughter. Comparing her efforts with the dedication of Shabnam's father, my mother felt secretly a bit guilty that she was not putting as much work in as Shabnam's father. Shabnam also had two private tutors for A-level maths: one from our school, who coached her to ensure she obtained the best mark in the school test; and another teacher whose job was to help her improve her marks for the examination board. Every one of us in my class shared this pressure to some degree; our miserable childhoods were occupied in running from one tutor to another at the end of every school day, in the evenings and at weekends. We barely had any time to have fun or play.

Though we didn't enjoy it, we all appreciated our parents' dedication. We understood that their worry stemmed from fear and uncertainty for the future. Our parents knew the pressures of working in areas of high competition, and fretted in precarious employment. Our country, which produces 200,000 school-leavers every year, can only provide higher education for 5,000 of them. The rest of the students have to retake the admissions test or are forced to pay to attend private institutions. Some have to leave higher education altogether. But parental support can go too far, leaving students dangerously vulnerable.

Shabnam had made her father proud by getting a place in the top medical school. However, her father was not a medic and couldn't study anatomy and physiology to keep helping his daughter. For the first time in her life she found herself unsupported and struggled in the lecture hall to follow the speaker and make her own notes. In the student accommodation, Shabnam was utterly helpless too, lacking any ability to look after herself. Her room was untidy and messy, her clothes thrown in a filthy tangle on the chair and dirty mugs piled up on the table. Her bed was never made. She had never been allowed to develop these skills. She couldn't even join in when, on rainy days, we'd huddle together on a bed and sing along to Tagore songs: she'd never had the freedom to spend her time listening to popular music.

Gradually Shabnam seemed to lose interest in life and withdrew into herself. While we were involved in the blood donation programme or volunteering for flood relief, she preferred to stay alone in her room. One day, Amartya Sen, the Nobel Laureate, came to visit Dhaka. I tried in vain to bribe Shabnam with my lecture notes to accompany me but she refused. Now she would sometimes just not turn up to our tutorials. She developed migraines and was prescribed glasses, her lovely eyes hidden behind the frame of her spectacles. Her plummeting self-esteem developed into depression, requiring psychiatric help during our first year.

We used to say she studied 'twenty-five hours a day' and 'the sun does not set on her empire' meaning that her reading light was always switched on. Unfortunately, she could not clear the first professional examination even after several attempts. Unable to cope, she abandoned her studies without graduating.

I heard that she had married a businessman but found it difficult to relate to her in-laws and could not develop a good relationship with her husband so, as her overprotective parents could not protect her marriage, she divorced. Finally Shabnam had the opportunity to become more independent after two successive failures, one in graduation and another in marriage.

Her father had done his best to build a bright future for his daughter and could not have known that all his effort and hyper involvement would prove so counterproductive. But ultimately – as so often happens in life – it was her failures that taught Shabnam self-reliance and strength, the most valuable lessons of all.

All for One Stitch

"Nirmala wants to be a surgeon? How dare she!"

She was our classmate, a dark skinned, slim-built Bengali girl of five-foot three. She was not attractive and we nicknamed her 'Conscience' after the character in medieval Bengali theatre who would appear between acts to tell the moral of the story to the audience. Nirmala was much too principled to ask anyone to cover for her if she was late to school and always refused to sign the attendance sheet for others.

She was always present at picnics, get-togethers, blood donation programmes or doing voluntary work for natural disasters. On our college trips, she was the first on the bus while we were still dilly-dallying in our rooms. Although we could trust her with our money and even our secrets, she was not very popular. We didn't really like her but had no reason to actually dislike her either.

She was just so eccentric: while we were flirting with our classmates or our lecturers, she would be writing four-page letters to her penpal in Paris. When we were memorising the causology and treatment of disease, we'd find her devouring Mills and Boon novels. While we were applying makeup for the cultural program, she was pestering us to go on a silent retreat in the yoga centre. When we were getting dressed up to celebrate Bangla New Year, she was more excited to recount for us the history and traditions relating to Pohela Boishakh. We sat through her lecture patiently. Her upbringing was entirely different from ours.

In our group fieldwork project, we all worked to collect data and two of our classmates wrote the assignment. She was asked to write the opening acknowledgment.

Our teacher, Dr Baten, was very pleased with it, telling her: "That's one of the most polished pieces of writing I have ever seen."

Nirmala said: "I didn't do much. I copied it from my father's library. I looked at all the English books and summarised most of the acknowledgements and wrote it out for you. There is nothing original or innovative."

Dr Baten was taken aback by her reply and we were all amazed that she couldn't even accept a teacher's praise.

During our internship, she declined to work in gynaecology; instead, she declared her interest in the surgical department.

One of the senior students, Nasrin, asked: "Why do you want to do surgery? You are like a dwarf trying to touch the moon."

Nirmala replied: "Surgery is not only for giant men, a little dwarf like me can also work in the surgical ward."

"You can earn way more money in obstetrics by palpating a uterus externally during pregnancy and internally during cesarean section. As a surgeon, you will never get any patients."

"I don't just work for money."

"You'll never build up a good practice! No patient will trust you."

Nirmala's voice was quiet but determined: "Trust is built from rapport. You don't need brute strength."

The surgical registrar, Dr Ali, was not entirely happy to see her on induction day. Usually, female interns came into surgery for two reasons: to avoid a heavy workload in the gynaecology and obstetrics ward or to avoid night duties. Typically, female surgical trainees are lazy and do this placement before leaving for the United States of America. In the long run, they will be very unlikely to pursue a career in surgery. Male interns, by contrast, work day and night to impress the registrar and to win opportunities in the operating theatre.

Nirmala broke the rules again.

She approached Dr Ali. "I would like to do night duties."

Dr Ali said, "Why do you need to do nights? It is not only female ward coverage, you have to cover male wards as well. It is not safe for you to work at night in the surgical ward with a male ward boy and male patients."

Nirmala said, "If you think that a female is at risk working at night in the top medical college hospital in Bangladesh, where in the world can she be safe?"

Dr Ali answered after a pause, "You understand, you'll need to do rectal digital examinations and male catheterisations at night with only a ward boy or a nurse."

"I do not think catheterisations or examinations change after dusk."

Dr Ali was not happy but eventually agreed, privately thinking that Nirmala would give up after working two or three weeks.

Nirmala did not follow the general rules. She worked hard, day and night. During a six months' internship, every intern will do at least one appendectomy. In her first month Nirmala spent her days in the outpatient clinic and admissions unit. Though her friend Jahangir had already done an appendectomy, Nirmala didn't get the chance to scrub (hand wash for five minutes, put on the sterile surgical gown and sterile gloves) even once.

Dr Ali said, "Nirmala, you should not scrub this month. There's no water supply, we have to use collected water."

Nirmala said, "Jahangir scrubbed on the last operating day."

Dr Ali answered with hesitation, "That day, I could not find any other assistant."

Month two: Nirmala was ready to scrub.

Dr Ali said, "Nirmala, you should not scrub today as there is shortage of sterile gowns."

During the third month, Dr Ali said, "Nirmala, I cannot allow you to do any cases because the patient couldn't buy enough suture material. We cannot waste this precious stuff for your log books."

Next weekend, during our weekly shopping trip, while the rest of us were browsing the make-up counter, Nirmala bought two sutures: one prolene and one silk, from the nearby pharmacy. She wished she could buy water and sterile gowns!

On the fourth month, Nirmala was allowed to scrub for a duodenal perforation.

Dr Ali requested, "Nirmala, come to the surgeon's side and hold the retractor. I cannot see anything; everything is so deep with all these layers of fat."

Nirmala was standing on tiptoes, holding the retractor with all her might and sweating profusely beneath her gown.

Dr Ali yelled out, "Oh no, we need one more prolene stitch! The patient didn't buy enough."

Nirmala replied promptly, "Don't worry, I have bought a prolene stitch and it is in the pocket of my apron."

Nirmala asked the nurse to reach into her apron pocket and get it out. The nurse opened the packet.

Dr Ali was in a rush, "I can't give you the stitches to do, the perforation is deep down and difficult to tie." Dr Ali used that suture to close the outer layer of the duodenum.

It was her last day on the surgical ward, Nirmala could not find any opportunity to do a skin closure, let alone an appendectomy. She had worked from early morning and had spent eight hours in the outpatient department and six hours in the admissions department, and at 10 pm she started her duties in emergency theatre.

Dr Ali announced, "Today is the last day for your surgical placement. Today, I shall give you an appendectomy to do."

Nirmala replied with hope and pleasure, "Yes, I admitted two appendicitis patients. I could do one."

Nirmala rushed to the scrub room and mentally prepared herself for doing the surgery.

During the operation, Dr Ali yelled, "Sh*t, the inflammation is so bad, I'll have to ligate and dissect out the appendix."

Nirmala answered without hesitation, "They should be inflamed! I can do it! We are not here to dissect the healthy appendix."

Dr Ali didn't reply.

Then Dr Ali became reasuring, "Do not worry, Nirmala, you can close the wound."

Not surprisingly, the patient had not bought any silk.

Dr Ali said, "We can use leftover silk from the sterile pot."

The so-called sterile pot was filled with Savlon and leftover threads which were kept for emergency use.

Nirmala told Dr Ali, "I do not want to use that thread. I bought silk with a hand-held needle."

When the suture was opened on the table, Dr Ali's eyes sparkled.

He said, "My God, Nirmala! You bought this expensive kit for this poor patient? I have never used one of these hand-held stitches. This three-centimetre wound needs three stitches: I will do the two corners. You can do the middle one."

Nirmala did the one stitch in the middle, at three o'clock in the morning, with tearful eyes.

Nirmala still wants to be a surgeon. She is determined, even though she knows how many hurdles she will need to overcome, and how many sacrifices she will need to make, to reach her goal.

A Mysterious Baby
in the Paediatric Ward

While I was an intern in the paediatric medicine ward, a baby was admitted one midnight. He was the healthiest and chubbiest in the whole unit with a fair complexion, melted-chocolate eyes and extraordinarily long, silken eyelashes. His curly, black hair and puffy, pink cheeks attracted the attention of everyone from the ward boy to the clinical lead. He was allocated to bed number ten: the nearest to the window, through which the whole city could be seen. The breeze blew in gently during the hot summer days.

Most of the babies were admitted with dysentery or coughs and colds, so it was no surprise to find him suffering from diarrhoea and vomiting. It was a common viral infection during the summer. Nevertheless, he was not severely dehydrated like other babies, and we were able to treat him with oral saline and baby food. He responded quickly. He was a very active and playful child, the happiest baby, with a spirited personality. He was tall for his age and naturally different from the rest of the babies in the hospital.

We were suspicious about him. He was brought to hospital by his grandmother, Julekha. She was a dark-skinned, short Bengali woman, unexceptional in every way. Her teeth were stained red from chewing betel leaf and betel nuts. Her black and white hair was slicked down with coconut oil. Her printed cotton sari was not clean. It was clear that she came from one of the nearby slum areas, without access to education or money. Sakina, the mother of the baby, arrived the next morning. She still seemed to be a teenager, and looked as destitute as her mother, sharing her complexion and build. She was wearing salowar kameez and covered her head with a dopatta. Her eyes were sunken with hollow-looking spaces and dark shadows under the lower eyelids. Sakina and her mother were not able to buy any baby food so we provided the necessities from the charity fund. Curious to find out more about them, we looked for the name of the father on the admission card: "Muhammad Hussein", which was not unusual. Our suspicion remained. We thought that the baby might have been stolen from a rich family and that his guardians were hiding this from us. The behaviour of the women was certainly a bit strange. Sakina was rather shy and did not speak much with the ward staff. She looked disturbed and exhausted, as if she wanted to hide from everyone and everything.

In the morning, we finished our ward round early. In the junior doctors' office, we were discussing the baby in bed number ten. Dr Hanna was obsessed with the whole affair: the behaviour and attitude of Julekha and Sakina had confused her a great deal. She was very keen to solve the whole matter and wanted to draw a definitive conclusion, so we decided to call Julekha and Sakina into our office for an interrogation:

Dr Hanna asked, "Where is this baby from? Where did you find him?"

Julekha answered, "He is my grandson."

"How can your grandson be so different from you? Where have you stolen the baby from? We will inform the police if you do not tell us the truth."

Sakina had been silent for the whole time, but now she started to cry.

Julekha insisted, "We are not liars. If you do not want to treat the baby, we will leave the hospital. Please discharge him."

Now we were reassured that they wanted to hide the baby from us and from the police. We tried harder to act like detectives.

Dr Hanna said, "So for the last two days, we have not seen the father, where is he?"

"His father is in Saudi Arabia."

It sounded like a lie.

Dr Hanna continued, "OK, the father is working in Saudi Arabia. No problem, just bring in any member of the father's family."

Julekha said, "We cannot bring anyone. None of them live in this country."

We were sure we knew the tricks, that our calculations were correct, that the baby was stolen.

At last Sakina sighed and said, "I went to Saudi Arabia as a domestic worker and the master is the father of the baby. I worked over there for two years. I was sacked when I became pregnant."

The room fell deadly quiet. We felt wretched thinking of the misery of the baby and the mother. We were ashamed of the conclusions we had lept to.

In the afternoon, our supervisor called all of us into his office for a meeting.

The supervisor asked, "So how's the baby in bed number ten?"

We answered, "He is doing well with good urine output, urea normalised, passed formed stool."

"I heard you all became detectives in the hospital".

We could not answer.

The supervisor said, "You are here to become doctors, not Sherlock Holmes. I do not want to hear any more gossip about baby smuggling. Do you understand me?"

"Yes, Sir."

By the time of the evening ward round, bed number ten was empty. The ward boy did not notice when Julekha and Sakina took the baby without consulting the doctors.

The British Embassy

Sukumar was preparing all the paperwork to apply for a visa for the UK. He was very pleased with his achievements, he bought a new folder from New Market, obtained bank statements from the Sonali Bank and photocopied all the necessary documents. On the way home from New Market, he met Mr Ajmal, one of his family friends. Mr Ajmal had been to London several times.

Mr Ajmal asked, "Sukumar, how are you? I have not seen you for so many years."

Sukumar replied, "I am fine, thank you. In fact, I am just planning to go to England."

"You have your visa?"

"I am off to the Embassy tomorrow. Today I came to make all my photocopies."

Mr Ajmal said, "Show me the paperwork".

After looking at the documents, he declared "No… You have only fifty thousand taka in your account: they will never give you a visa. You need to show at least two hundred thousand taka."

Sukumar's heart sank. "Where can I find that amount of money overnight?"

Mr Ajmal reassured him, "Go to the Messrs. Rahman photocopy shop, they will make fake bank statements in an hour."

"Are you sure that would work?"

Mr Ajmal said, "l am confident the officer would never call the bank. They just want to see the amount in your account."

Following Mr Ajmal's advice, Sukumar had fake bank statements prepared, showing his bank-balance as being two hundred thousand taka.

On Monday, Sukumar appeared at seven in the morning in front of the British Embassy in Gulshan, Dhaka. He found himself in seventieth place in the queue. That day, the thirtieth person in the queue was allowed to enter through the gate. Sukumar was disheartened but didn't give up. On Tuesday, he arrived an hour earlier and was still the sixtieth in the queue. Disappointed, he tried to find out what time people started queuing every day. He noticed a man in a khaki costume moving about the queue. People were calling him Mansur.

Sukumar asked him, "Can you please tell me when I should come to get to the front of the line?"

Mansur answered, "You will never get through the gate even if you come at three in the morning."

"Why not? How do I get through, then?"

"You have to buy a space from me. I stay here, and put a brick at the front space before anybody queues. You have to pay me five hundred taka, double if it is a visa for the USA."

Sukumar wasn't satisfied with Mansur's offer. He believed that the UK wasn't a country of corruption and nepotism but a place where everything was fair and transparent. He phoned the Home Office. He was told by the official that they couldn't do anything to manage the crowd outside the office but if Sukumar had experienced any hassle once he was inside the Embassy, he should call back. After getting this unhelpful reply, he angrily paid Mansur five hundred taka.

On Wednesday, Sukumar arrived at eight in the morning and found that Mansur had bought a place for him in front of the queue from one of the racketeers letting people through. On his third attempt, he was admitted to the British Embassy.

The office was very tidy with a touch of greenery in every corner. Sukumar saw several villagers in the office applying for visas. He wondered how these guys would communicate in English and was disappointed not to meet any more sophisticated or quality people. In the waiting room, the man sitting next to him started to talk, introducing himself as Jalil.

Jalil asked, "Is this the first time you are going to England?"

Sukumar said, "I am applying for a visa for the first time. I have never been to the UK".

Jalil went on, "Do you know anyone in the UK? I have been refused twice but the officers will issue visas for those who have relatives there. Family contacts count far more than education: I bet those villagers over there will get permanent residency in the UK before we do."

Sukumar was called by the officer to his desk. An interpreter was also sitting beside the officer.

The officer asked, "Why do you want to go to England?"

"I would like to apply to university there."

The officer asked to see his paperwork. Hesitantly, Sukumar pushed his fake statement across the desk.

The interpreter asked "How on earth did you get two thousand taka in the last six months?"

Sukumar pretended he could not hear and ignored him. The interpreter hadn't stated anything for him to disagree with.

A six-month visa was issued. Sukumar was over the moon. He wanted to run around telling everyone that he was going to visit the Queen. Lost in a happy daydream, he imagined himself bumping into celebrities on every street corner of London.

Nowadays things are different. If you want to travel to the UK, you have to submit your papers to the local office and they are sent on to New Delhi to be processed. This makes things even harder, since in India they prioritise their own citizens.

The Green Passport

We, thousands of doctors from the Indian subcontinent, were all gathered in Eastham, London with only one objective: to pass the Professional Linguistic Assessment Board exam (PLAB) for registration in the General Medical Council (GMC). More than eighty per cent of candidates were from India, the rest were from other countries such as Pakistan, Bangladesh, Myanmar and Sri Lanka. Our reading room was as cosmopolitan as the streets of London. One day, in Eastham library, my study partner asked to see my passport. I was surprised when he told me that he did not know the Bangladeshi passport is green. He also informed me that most Muslim countries use green passports, as green is considered to be the favourite colour of the Prophet Muhammad. I used to think that the green symbolised the paddy-fields and the lush vegetation of Bangladesh. That day I learned that my passport labels me as a Muslim, despite being a Buddhist. I realised that the discrimination does not only come about as a result of colour, race and gender; even your passport colour matters.

I can tell you the trials of having a green passport in different airports. I have visited so many countries, but this was only possible as I had indefinite leave to remain in the UK. Still, the inconvenience was extreme.

Entering Canada from the United States, the conversation was very edgy.

The Canadian border office demanded, "So, you are from Bangladesh? You want to stay in Canada for three nights to visit Toronto, Quebec and Montreal?"

I answered, "Yes."

"How much money do you have?"

I was perplexed. "I have already booked my hotel but I have 100 Canadian dollars in cash, plus my bank card."

The officer asked, "Can you afford three nights in Canada, coming from Bangladesh?"

I was getting angry now. "For your information, though I have a green passport, I work in England and my salary is double yours. This is my ID, not my bank statement."

The officer stared and stamped my passport with sullen rage.

The misery at the French Embassy in Edinburgh was unbelievable. I had to queue for seven consecutive days for a one-week Schengen visa. As a child, I took French lessons with the Alliance Française. My teenage fantasies were all about French teachers: they seemed so softly spoken and polite, but the officer at the embassy completely ruined the image. I had learned a couple of slang words in French and really wished I could use them on this guy.

In the John F Kennedy International Airport, New York, I had to take an oath not to harm anyone in America before getting my passport stamped. As a Buddhist, I chant five precepts every day and the first one is not to harm any sentient being. That day, I chanted on the border not to harm any American citizen or property and we missed our connecting flight from New York to San Francisco because it took five hours to finish all these formalities while the officers were still looking for my criminal records. The misery of holding a green passport!

In Berlin, the German border officer harassed me for more than an hour.

The officer asked, "With this passport, why are you coming here only for two nights?"

I replied, "I am here to attend a conference. I have a return ticket. After my lecture, I will leave Germany."

"Do you have any criminal record?"

"Do I look like a criminal?"

"Do you have any convictions?"

"For what?"

"You are holding a green passport; we need to scrutinize it. Take your seat in the side room. We will call you later."

I passed a very anxious hour in a deserted Berlin Brandenburg Airport.

My only hassle-free journey took me from Belfast to Dublin. I'd applied for a Schengen visa for a job interview, but it was still not issued by the day of my flight. Friends advised me to get a passenger train from Belfast to Dublin and pretend to be a commuter: the officers do not ask for your passport unless you look like a suspect. I tucked away my unused plane ticket and bought a train ticket instead. At Belfast's Great Victoria Street train station, I picked up a copy of *The Guardian* and a cappuccino, studying the newspaper attentively for the entire 130-minute journey between the two Irelands. My return trip similarly passed without incident. I escaped the border check and cheated the border officers on this occasion, though I would have been prosecuted if I had been caught with the green passport and might have spent a night in Her Majesty's prison. My retribution came in due course – I did not get the job.

Now, I have changed colour. Though I cannot alter my skin, through British citizenship my passport has gone from green to blue. The border officers don't dare quiz me about my earnings, my intentions on entering a country or even require me to take an oath. Clearly this shift in the colour spectrum marks me out as a better citizen of planet Earth.

The Library

Arshad and Sajal had enrolled for a postgraduate degree. They travelled from their village and rented a room near the Kamalapur Railway Station after leaving their student accommodation. The room didn't have any space in which to put a chair and table for studying, and the noise of the trains disturbed the occupants from early morning until midnight. As undergraduates at small colleges, they had enjoyed quiet study rooms on campus, but now they would have to find somewhere else. They planned to spend every day in the University Library, where they could study quietly.

The University Library was a large building, housing a huge collection of books. Most of them were old editions: newer editions were rarely available and usually allowed to be used only in the library, and not taken out on loan. One afternoon, the library front desk was empty because the librarian had disappeared to sleep off his lunch. Arshad took a book from the shelf and had a look, and noticed it was missing several chapters: someone had cut its pages out with a blade. Most of the books were so ancient that their pages had turned yellow. In some books, pages had been nibbled by bookworms; in others, important paragraphs had been cut out by competitive students. Arshad struggled to find a useful book in a useable condition.

Arshad and Sajal were disappointed but instead of giving up, they went to Nilkhet to buy books. Nilkhet was the book market: hundreds of bookstalls were selling pirate copies, illicit and unauthorised reproductions. It was not possible for the poorest students in Bangladesh to buy current editions because of the prohibitive cost: Nilkhet was the solution. Arshad and Sajal bought photocopies of the latest editions of all their essential books.

On the second day of January, Arshad and Sajal returned to the library. The librarian was a middle-aged man with a big, bald head, chewing a betel nut, with a warm cup of tea steaming beside him on his desk. He wore a grey pullover and had a striped scarf wrapped around his neck.

He did not appear glad to see the newcomers. He said they would need to pay if they wanted a library card: as Arshad had seen the condition of the books last week, he decided not to bother. The librarian told them that they could use the study area without a card if they found a space. He seemed to cheer up once it was clear he wouldn't have to do any work.

The two students walked over to the study area and were surprised to see that every seat was reserved even though many didn't have anyone sitting there. Many seats had been chained with locks, so that only the key-holder could use the chairs and tables. Arshad and Sajal left the study area in great despair. In the corridor they spotted Khalil, one of the senior students from their college. Khalil was involved in student politics, had not worked to complete his course but had finally obtained his degree at his third attempt, thanks only to political influence. They were surprised to see him in the library because he had not touched a single book during the course of his studies: they wondered if he was looking for a future bride in the library or had some plan to gain political power by rubbing shoulders with future leaders.

Khalil yelled out, "How are you guys?"

Sajal answered, "Fine. We were looking for a seat in the study area, but we've given up. All the spaces are occupied."

Khalil replied after a pause, "You will have to wait until the exams are over."

Arshad asked, "Do you know who chained the chairs?"

"The librarian sells the study spaces to students. They are chained to prevent anyone else using them if the owners are late or absent."

"We never thought it would be so difficult to find a place to study," Arshad said. "Can you please help us to find some seats?"

Khalil replied, "These spaces have been occupied by the same individuals for a year or more. I don't think you have the least hope until next January. You could try to bribe the librarian and see what he can do. I can't think of any alternative."

Arshad and Sajal felt frustrated and fed up. They couldn't face the thought of bribing the librarian just to get a place to study. They left the library with their bags full of their pirate textbooks. The students were coming to the library to occupy the study area just as the river pirates came to seize the land. Defeated for today, Arshad and Sajal vowed to continue the fight. Who'd have thought that the struggle for a place to sit in the library would be fiercer and even more competitive than the fight to get accepted into the university itself?

A Five Cent Pickle

Kiron was in primary school; she was seven years old. She had been brought up in a strict, disciplinarian household and both she and her elder sister Juthi – with whom she was very close – were scared of their parents. Unlike their friends they were not allowed to wear gold earrings and were never given pocket money. They resented their parents' hardness toward them, which they felt was extremely unfair.

The two sisters used to travel to school by rickshaw for a fare of one taka and fifty cents. At break, they had to eat home-made snacks and were not allowed to buy anything from the vendors. After school, Kiron always wanted to play for a while with her friend Sanjib but never could, because her mother would be anxious and angry if she was late home from school. Also, every day their grandfather would be at the house waiting for their return, as he gave English and maths lessons to Juthi who was preparing for her scholarship examination late that year. Kiron did not like the old man at all because the lessons meant that she couldn't play with Juthi. Instead, her grandfather would make her practice doing sums in addition and subtraction to keep her busy.

One day, returning home in the rickshaw, the two sisters were chatting.

Kiron said, "I wish I could buy some sweets from the vendors' carts. Sanjib buys sweets from the vendors every single day."

Juthi replied, "Mum won't be pleased if she knows you are greedy and spend your time staring at other children's food."

Kiron questioned, "What does 'greedy' mean?"

"Greedy means you want too much for yourself, and that is not good."

From that day, Kiron played in the school playground and never looked at the vendors' trolleys. She was terrified that her mother would be able to guess her thoughts, and that anger would flash from her eyes.

One day, Juthi forgot to give the full one taka and fifty cents to the rickshawala. During her class, she found a five-cent coin deep down in the pocket of her school uniform. At breaktime, Juthi saw that her sister was on her own in the playground. Kiron was not looking cheerful.

Juthi asked, "Are you all right, Kiron? Where are your friends?"

Kiron replied, "Off buying treats from the vendors. You told me not to look at them while they were enjoying their sweets. I don't want to be greedy, and don't want to make Mum angry."

"Well, little sister, I can treat you today."

Kiron perked up a little but looked doubtful still. "How can you buy anything without any money?"

Juthi answered happily, "I've got five cents left in my pocket from the rickshaw fare."

"Are you sure Mum will not know about it?"

Juthi laughed, "How will she know if we don't tell her?"

"Okay, I promise not to tell her."

They happily walked towards the vendors' trolleys on which a lot of goodies were spread out: toffees, candies, chocolates, biscuits, cakes and pickles. Their eyes were dazzled by so many options. However, every single thing cost more than five cents.

Juthi looked disappointed and said regretfully, "I'm sorry, Kiron I don't think we can buy any sweets with five cents."

"Are you sure? Have you checked properly?"

Juthi replied, "They all are placed in order of price, look."

Kiron was upset.

Juthi said after a while, during which she'd scanned the trolleys again: "There are the pickles. It says they're five cents each."

Kiron did not like sour flavours much but she agreed to try it.

Juthi bought a pickle. It was the size of a small coin and they carefully divided it in two. They ate the sweet-and-sour treat as slowly as they could, and afterwards Juthi gave the wrapper to Kiron. The paper was silver-coloured and shiny. Kiron folded it and kept it safe like a treasure, deep in her pocket. They were both happy. Little did they know that this little treat would turn out to be the forerunner of a big tragedy.

At the weekend, while her mother was washing the school dresses, she found the shiny treasure in Kiron's pocket.

Her mother asked, "Why have you got a pickle wrapper?"

Kiron could not believe that she had forgotten to take the treasure from her pocket. She could not tell a lie or make up a story and replied with tearful eyes, "Juthi bought the pickle from the school vendor."

Mum asked angrily, "Where did she get the change?"

Kiron replied, "A five cent coin was left in her pocket from the rickshaw fare."

Mum called Juthi from her room. "You short-changed the rickshawala. Why did you not find him and give him his five cents?"

Juthi replied, "It was a mistake! And I only realised while I was sitting in class."

Mum said, "It wasn't your money. Why didn't you return it to me? Why did you buy something from the vendors?" She went on, "Your greediness will end badly for you one of these days. You don't know what the vendors do. Their treats might have been spiked with drugs that could make you very sick. They will take you away from your parents. Do you want that?"

The girls didn't feel the least bit guilty. They couldn't imagine anything worse happening to them in life than they were already undergoing, having to live in their house under their mother's military regime. They'd be glad to be taken away from parents who treated them so cruelly.

The following Monday, the teacher announced to all the children that Sanjib had not returned home from school on Friday night. He had been kidnapped. Kiron did not understand what 'kidnapped' meant but remembered her mother's warning when Juthi explained to her the meaning of the word. After that incident, no vendors were allowed on the school premises.

There was a police enquiry during which Sanjib's parents came into school several times. They looked so sad and scared that Kiron felt sorry for them and decided to forgive her mother. The following year, Sanjib was rescued from the United Arab Emirates. He had been sold by child traffickers to the Middle East where he had been forced to work as a camel jockey.

The Storm

One year, in early October, Komol's father decided to take his family to Cox's Bazar. Komol was ten years old and one of the brightest students his class, brighter even than his brother Amol, two years his senior. They were given special leave from school. Komol proudly told his friends that he was going to visit Cox's Bazar to enjoy the beach.

The class teacher, who'd authorised the leave, said, "The tourist season has not started yet. It's not the best time to go, the ocean will be very rough and the sky cloudy. You could visit Teknaf and Saint Martin's island but two days will not be enough."

Komol could only answer, "My father decided to stay for just two nights."

They were four of them in the car: the brothers Komol and Amol with their mother and father. Komol was extremely excited at the thought of visiting the natural, unbroken, sandy beach which, at ninety-six miles, is the longest in the world. But it was not pleasant accompanying his serious-faced father who always seemed to spoil his fun. Komol believed that his father's mission in life was to criticise him and make him feel stupid, and that was why he plagued him with thousands of questions about the minutest of things. His mother and Amol also felt the same.

The journey started at seven o'clock in the morning.

After leaving Chittagong city, Amol requested, "Can we turn on the music in the car?"

Father replied, "We're not going on a picnic."

Mother tried to take Amol's side and said, "Although it's not a picnic, we are not going to a funeral. The boys want to listen to some music, let them have a bit of fun."

Father only said, "You spoil those boys."

There was silence in the car for a while.

Then father said, "If you can answer my questions, the music can be turned on."

Amol, Komol and their mother knew that he was up to his tricks as usual.

Father asked, "Where does the name Cox's Bazar come from?"

They had never thought about it. They knew that it had the longest beach, the Bay of Bengal, Rohingya Refugees, a harbour, the Naf River and a fish market but had never wondered about the origin of its name.

Father went on, "Didn't your teacher tell you about all of this in your lessons? There is no point in getting the highest marks in your examinations if you don't know the basics of your own culture, heritage and history."

Father continued, "The original name of the area was Palongkee. Cox's Bazar is named after a superintendent of the British East India Company called Captain Hiram Cox. He kept a journal and wrote a book about the role he played in settling the conflict between the Rakhaine and Arakanese refugees between 1766 and 1799. Our people honoured his work and named the area Cox's Bazar…"

Amol asked, "Was he English?"

Father replied, "Don't interrupt! Does it matter whether he was Scottish, Welsh or Irish? He was appointed by the East India Company and came from England."

Mother was wondering if it really mattered whether the area was called Palongkee or Cox's Bazar but didn't dare say it aloud.

Amol asked another silly question, "Father, although the British invaded us, are all the English bad?"

Father replied after a big sigh, "Listen, the British East India Company invaded Bengal in 1757. The enmity between the Bengali communities and the conspiracy in the Bengal Sultanate were contributing factors, and the invaders were cunning in taking full advantage. If it hadn't been the British, it would have been someone else, and we might have been a Portuguese, French or Dutch colony. Then the history of India would have unfolded differently. In one respect we are fortunate that we were colonised by the British, but that's another story."

His father realised that no one was interested in his lecture and turned on the music since no answers to his question, right or wrong, had been attempted.

Around midday, they arrived in Cox's Bazar and headed directly to the beach. Although it was autumn, the daytime temperature was averaging thirty to thirty two degrees celsius. The sultry heat and high humidity made the whole family sweat. They needed to take shelter from the sun's glare, so they went to the shade of the nearby stores for a while and then returned to the hotel.

In the evening, when the temperature had cooled down slightly, they went back to the beach to watch the sunset. The sky was cloudy but they felt refreshed by the gentle breeze, and were excited to see the waves and hear the sound of the ocean. While Amol was taking pictures of his mother in the water, the camera slipped from his hands into the sea. It stopped working because of the salt water, so they could not take any more pictures that night.

Komol's father had planned for them to visit a famous monastery in Ukhiya the next morning, thirty kilometres south of Cox's Bazar. They reached Ukhiya after midday. It was another cloudy day with high humidity.

By the late afternoon, it had started to rain. The rain quickly became an incessant downpour, accompanied by a strong, gusty wind. The gale was so violent that trees were uprooted, blocking the main highway. The storm lasted for forty-five minutes but the torrential rain continued.

The abbot of the monastery advised Komol's father to stay in Ukhiya overnight as the weather was too bad to drive back to Cox's Bazar. A man from the village offered them shelter for the night though unfortunately he had no beds in his house. The family was shown into their room and given pillows and bedsheets, with space made for them to sleep on the floor. There was no electricity so they spent a pitch-black night in a stranger's house. It started to rain again and intermittent thunder and lightning continued throughout the night. They missed their comfortable beds.

Komol and Amol were scared of the sound of the storm and clung to their mother.

Komol whispered, "Father, I'm frightened. I want to go back to the hotel."

Father agreed, "Yes, me too. We have booked luxurious rooms in the hotel. But 'what is destined, cannot be denied'. We have ended up on a mud floor in a village hut."

The next morning, they returned to Cox's Bazar and collected their luggage from the hotel. They drove back home and returned to school the next day. Komol and Amol were very disappointed to have nothing to tell their friends about their journey or their visit to the famous beach. The broken camera meant that they didn't even have any pictures to show the class.

"I think the boys are very upset," Mother said sadly. "Those boys are still too young to understand that what is destined cannot be denied," their serious father answered gravely.

The Girl I Remember

The girl was called Lakshmi, named after the goddess of wealth. She was our classmate in the second year at school and sat on the last bench, furthest from the teacher's desk. She was very thin and shabby, ribs and collarbones visible through her uniform and her cheekbones prominent beneath dry skin. She wore faded clothes and canvas shoes, with dirty socks peeping through the rips and holes. Her teeth were rust-coloured from the well water used by the people of the shanty town who were denied access to the purified water supplied to the townspeople. Her gums were stained by the coal she used in place of toothpaste. Lakshmi's old, navy-blue school dress had passed through generations of previous students and was faded through excessive washing and drying in the sun, its white belt weak now, its buttons loose and unmatched in their sagging buttonholes. We other students all had thick, black hair but hers was listless and reddish brown. Our uniform code stipulated white ribbons in our plaits, but hers were rusty auburn from the well water. The truth is that poverty was exposed in every aspect of her appearance. Even our fancy plastic tiffin boxes mocked her polythene bag holding the dry brown rotis and molasses of her midday meal, for which we all had sandwiches or pancakes. She did not have a water bottle but used to drink water from the taps in the toilets.

We convent-school students were all from upper middle-class or middle-class families. Our parents had to pay a great deal of money in school fees, which helped the committee to run the school. Only the converted Christian community and the churchgoers were allowed to attend this missionary school without paying fees. Lakshmi was the daughter of our school Ayah, who used to clean the toilets. The term "Ayah" is considered polite and respectful in our language, though it can be used to mean a servant or a maid. Lakshmi was granted admission due to her mother's job and was completely mismatched in our class. She never played with anyone during breaktime but used to visit her mother instead, preferring to spend time with her mother rather than her classmates. The teacher scolded her for every little thing, though in the minds of the school administration these were far from trivial – for instance, we were asked every year to bring toys and toiletries for the Meena Bazaar. The school teachers organized everything, setting up their own stalls to sell clothes, jewellery, handicrafts and snacks, which went for high prices. But Lakshmi could not manage to get anything from home for the Meena Bazaar. She could never contribute to our homework of sharing a piece of news from the daily newspaper, as her parents did not take a newspaper. For the cultural programme, we were asked to make a fairy costume and buy Japanese hand fans for a dance. She could not manage to get the dress or the hand fans. The teacher was not happy with this.

In Bengal, different dialects mark out our regions. At school we had to speak in an elegant Bangla, formal and standardised like BBC English or Received Pronunciation. We were not allowed to speak in the distinctive Chittagong dialect at school or home, in fear of losing the accent of privilege, those hard-won Bangla consonants Bha, kha, ttha.

If the teacher asked Lakshmi to recite simple sentences – Teacher: "Ami bhath khai (I eat rice)", Lakshmi: "Ami bath kai" – it would always degenerate into the teacher bellowing "BHath , KHai!"

Lakshmi's English pronunciation was even more lamentable, "I am in class two" turning into "I am in callous toe."

The teacher used to call her "Gheo Bhut", meaning a country pumpkin. Every afternoon, we heard the same chorus. She couldn't do it correctly in spite of practice at school as she did not have anybody to help her at home. Lakshmi could barely understand and follow the teaching in class. Every day, she dreaded showing the teacher her homework and we felt sorry for her. Our class teacher smacked her with the ruler because Lakshmi was unable to complete the comprehension test. Her handwriting was messy and illegible. The teacher called it "Kaker theng er boker theng": chicken scratches. She did not want to hand over the notebook to the teacher. She resisted doing it in fear of impending doom.

One day our classmate, Bulbul, peed on the floor. Our irascible teacher roared and sent someone to fetch the Ayah. There was a long delay in responding to the call. In the meantime, the urine trickled over the whole classroom floor. Lakshmi's mother eventually arrived to clean up, though Lakshmi stared away, avoiding her eye. I realised she was ashamed of her mother's job.

The day before the summer holidays, there was a road traffic accident in front of the school. A crowd gathered and people were shouting. We saw someone dragging the Ayah from the scene, wailing and pounding her fist into her chest. Before I realised anything, my mother pulled me home. My mother, usually so remote, gave me a hug for a long time. Eventually, she told me never to cross the road without an adult at my side.

The next morning, at school assembly, one minute's silence was observed for Lakshmi. She could not afford ice cream so she had been buying "Kulfi" from the kulfiwala when a bus ran her over, cracking her skull, spilling the grey and white matter across the black pitch of the road. Lakshmi's much-reviled brain was now a stain on the street. Sanitation workers had to come to hose the ground clean. This time, Lakshmi was humiliated because her brain stained the street, as well as being unable to memorise classic pronunciations of Bangla and the Queen's English.

By now, reincarnation will have taken place. Lakshmi, who suffered cruelly from the hardships of life, must surely have been reborn a goddess enjoying every privilege. Her soul hardly deserves eternal punishment.

Our Pet, Klusener

When we moved to our new house, everyone advised us to get a dog. Our house was on the edge of the city. The area was surrounded by green land and paddy fields. Our new home was like an eagle's nest in the woodland. So for the sake of safety, we needed to have a dog who would bark not only at thieves but also at any strangers. He would sound the alarm for us, as we lived on the edge of nowhere.

My mother asked Atul, our orderly, to look around the neighbourhood for a puppy. There was no need to go to a pet shop to buy a dog: strays are common and usually have litters of seven or eight, so there's never any trouble finding a dog. My mother specifically requested a white puppy: not brown, red or black. Days passed and Atul could not find one white puppy although we were eagerly waiting. Eventually, after a few weeks, Atul came up the drive with our puppy in his arms.

We couldn't find a suitable Bengali name. In those days my family was crazy about cricket, so we decided to choose either Man of the Match 'Shane Warne' or the best player of the series, Lance Klusener. My sister decided on "Klusener" because of Lance Klusener's exciting batting style – and besides, "Shane Warne" was rather long – though Klusener was never easy to pronounce with a Bengali accent. The puppy was a South Asian pye dog (deshi Kukur). His eyes were almond-shaped and dark brown in colour against his soft, white coat. His ears were luxuriously floppy during his puppyhood. His tail was curled and held high when he was excited. He was an inquisitive and playful ball of fluff.

As he was taken away from his mother soon after his birth, we had to feed him cow's milk. Then the next problem arose: he didn't make any noise or bark. He had been brought to bark for us, but didn't do his job! We thought he might be dumb, but that could not be tested. We would try to encourage him by saying, "Woof, woof!" We did not know that the canine vocalizations usually begin at around twelve to sixteen weeks of age. And indeed, when he was three months old, he finally started to bark.

He was an extremely friendly, lively dog with a sweet disposition, which made him a great companion. The dog was well looked after and liked to eat bread, biscuits, rice, fish or meat curry. He formed strong social bonds with us and was always thrilled to see us. He became particularly attached to my father, following him wherever he went. My father became the centre of his universe. Klusener would always lounge by his table throughout the day, resting against his feet. Next to his books, Klusener became my father's best friend. Their relationship was more than a terrestrial one.

One day we couldn't find Klusener anywhere. We scoured the neighbourhood, calling his name with no response. All day we could not find him and we were very upset: then Atul came with the news that he had been taken by our neighbours. He was so adorable that they had stolen him. We asked them to return the dog. The neighbour told

Atul that they were feeding him beef, which annoyed us immensely. But when Atul informed them that we'd fed Klusener pork, they immediately released him: from that point on he would never be touched by the neighbours. However, for security, we kept him chained in the driveway.

In the autumn, our chauffeur became ill so we needed a new one. A candidate to be our new driver came to the house for a test. Unfortunately he ran over Klusener's left hind leg while reversing, as his chain had prevented the puppy from running out of the way. His fractured leg was set in plaster – and the driver did not get the job. As he left, he told Atul that he would slaughter all the street dogs as the puppy had cost him the job.

Klusener became part of our family. He barked at every strange noise, even the chirps of crickets. None of the cats and birds in the vicinity could walk over our lawns due to his vigilant eyes and ears. Everyone was scared of entering our house, not only because of his barking, but also because he jumped up at them. Jumping was his way of greeting. Our paperboy had a fight with him every day – and often Klusener would chew up the entire front page. Once a potential bridegroom for my elder sister came to pay a visit to our house but couldn't get through the gate due to Klusener. He kept wanted and unwanted guests away from our house and was always the first to defend us. Atul would take him to the city cooperation office for his annual vaccination, though we never needed pet insurance and never had to clear up his messes.

Early one winter, my mother could not find Klusener. He was later found dead in the back yard, a victim of poisoning. We were all so attached to him that it was difficult to bear the loss. We never kept another pet. The lease was very short and was over in the blink of an eye. In his short time with us, Klusener taught us unconditional love and filled us with warmth and excitement. His departure blasted a crater in our hearts so that we failed to anticipate the forthcoming tragic turn of events.

A couple of months later, we lost our father unexpectedly. Klusener did not grieve the loss of his master. He had gone ahead to guide him into the afterlife and accompany him there.

End